PRAISE FOR THE ART OF THE HOOK UP

'Wolf gives a confidence boost to anyone looking to deliver a mind-blowing performance in the bedroom. No-nonsense advice from Australia's most authentic sex expert... and the perfect gift for your next Tinder match!'

Alita Brydon, founder of Bad Dates of Melbourne

'It's packed solid with so much good stuff, without feeling crowded or rushed.'

Pete, 55

'I recommend the shit out of this book. As a sex therapist I spend a lot of time discussing communication skills; the suggestions and examples are perfect, and apply as much to long-term relationships as to hook ups.'

Linda Kirkman, PhD, sexologist

'I've spent time with Georgie both in and out of the bedroom, and can honestly say that this is a person who practices what they preach. This book will teach you to navigate hook ups like a professional without leaving you feeling over-whelmed or under-prepared. Your dating life will thank you.'

Alice Grey, Melbourne Escort

'This book shows how sex isn't something you do to someone, but something you do together. It provides a valuable insight into what women want from sex.'

Dave, 33

THE ART OF THE HOOK UP

YOUR STRAIGHTFORWARD GUIDE TO A SUCCESSFUL SEX LIFE

GEORGIE WOLF

Published in Australia by Convergence Press

PO Box 3, Abbotsford VIC 3067 | info@artofthehookup.com | www.artofthehookup.com

A catalogue record for this book is available from the National Library of Australia

ISBN: 978-0-6485842-0-9

Editing by Tender L Creative | www.tenderlcreative.com.au

Printed by IngramSpark Australia

TABLE OF CONTENTS

ACKNOWLEDGEMENTS

Writing a book is like tending a garden–it requires regular bursts of enthusiasm and a liberal amount of patience. I'm not much of a gardener; I prefer rolls in the hay to watering the flowers. Luckily, I have a wonderful team who have nurtured this project and helped bring it to fruition.

I'd like to offer thanks to the friends who shared their stories and to everyone who gave feedback on early drafts.

I owe much gratitude to Greg and Pete for their brilliant suggestions. To Linda, for her compassionate sexpertise. To Liv, for her lightning-fast editing. To Fiona, for getting me into shape as a non-fiction writer ('What's it REALLY about?')

The enthusiasm of my curious, sex-positive community has made all the difference. I love our bubble, folks–let's make it bigger!

Last, I'd like to thank my biological family for supporting my interesting lifestyle choices… and my alternative family, Rog, Tess, and Anita, for being my champions.

INTRODUCTION

Last night, I had the best sex of my life.

My date and I hung out at a beach-side bar. It was the first time we'd met each other face-to-face—he rolled up to the kerb on his motorcycle, sat down next to me, ordered us both a beer, and within minutes we were talking like old friends. We shared drinks, playful touches, the intimate details of our lives. The connection was undeniable.

When we got naked back at my hotel, we discovered that we were perfect for each other: bodies in sync, I felt wholly alive. At the end of the night, he left with a smile.

To the casual observer, I'm just an average thirty-something woman with a sparkle in my eyes and a swing in my step. But the truth is, I'm a total hook-up champion.

I'm like the sexual secret service—working undercover, prepared for any situation. I'll flirt with anyone I find interesting: strangers in public, guys on Tinder, ladies at parties. Within minutes of meeting a potential partner, I can work out if they're right for me… and when I like someone, I approach them with confidence. I've banged metal band guitarists, enjoyed wild kink sessions, and picked up at sex clubs. My goal is to craft the perfect encounter: adventurous, connected, sexy as fuck.

You might wonder, what kind of person does this stuff? Women don't enjoy casual sex, do they? Do these sorts of crazy adventures happen, besides in porn clips and our own fantasies? I'm here to tell you, dreams come true… and I've elevated sex to an art form.

We, my friend, are living in the golden age of the hook up—those sexual encounters that are too short or too casual to be romantic relationships. Sometimes they begin online, sometimes in person. Either way, they're part of modern life.

Modern singles are more sexually adventurous than ever. We're waiting until later in life to settle down, and casual flings are commonplace. Dating apps allow us to view the profiles of thousands of potential partners. Ideas that used to be on the sexual fringe—kink, non-monogamy, swinging, threesomes—now appear in the daily news, and by God, do we want it!

But when I talk to my friends about their hook ups, one thing becomes clear: our attempts to get laid aren't always working. They complain:

'When I say I'm just looking for sex, guys treat me like shit.'

'Women won't talk to me online… what am I doing wrong?'

'He seemed like a nice guy, then something awful happened…'

'How do I ask for a one-night-stand without freaking people out?'

I know how it feels. I wasn't always a hook-up expert… ten years ago, my sex life was a total train wreck.

I was keen to get sexy, but I didn't know what I was doing. I was socially awkward and treated my partners carelessly. And who could blame me; nobody teaches us this stuff, right? As I blundered through my twenties trying to get laid, I suffered one disaster after another. I slept with people who put me down, refused to use condoms, and left without saying goodbye. I felt ashamed when I couldn't pick up, and guilty when I did. I was pressured into sex I didn't want, and—worst of all—I sometimes pressured my partners, too.

From excruciatingly awkward dates to threesomes gone wrong… if there's a way to fuck up sex, I've probably done it. I didn't know how to do better so I faked bravado, hoping nobody would notice I was winging it.

So, what changed? How did I stop being an awkward and become a sexual superstar? In short, I became a sex worker.

In my late twenties, I embarked on a career as an escort, levelling up on my sexual knowledge. My job demands a specific set of skills—a good sex worker isn't just someone who swaps sexy services for money. Rather, we are the elite, front-line troops of sex, adept at helping people have better experiences. On a typical workday I might spend an hour with a nervous divorcee, teach a young couple how to get kinky, help a woman experiment with bisexuality, or assist a young guy in losing his virginity. These situations have one thing in common: I must ensure everyone has a great time.

To do my job well, I needed to learn new skills. I read books on sex education. I signed up for kink and Tantra workshops. I studied my clients, working out how to give them the experiences they needed. I had a LOT of sex, both paid and unpaid.

These efforts had incredible benefits. Not only did I become a successful escort, my personal sex life improved. I found people I genuinely liked and learned to stay away from the ones I didn't. I picked up more and had better sex. Best of all, I began to walk away from my encounters feeling happy, rather than guilty. I was learning what good hook ups are all about.

Have you ever wished picking up was less nerve-wracking? Do you struggle to find people who treat you with respect? Have you ever been in an awkward, naked situation? If so, this book can help. It's a decade of my hard-won experienced, repackaged as useful skills anyone can use.

To me, a successful hook up means:

1. **Finding the right people**—those you click with and find attractive.
2. **Negotiating amazing sex.**
3. **Going your separate ways** in a manner that leaves everyone better off.

Here's how it happens. Like all good adventures, our journey towards better hook ups requires the right protective equipment. Part I of this book gives you the psychological armour to feel confident. In Part II, I'll put you in the driver's seat of your own sex life, with skills to steer your encounters in the right direction. And Part III details the advanced knowledge that will transform you into a sexual superhero, ready to fuck the world into better shape.

This book is for everyone. Guys, girls, whoever… the stuff in here is useful no matter what you have in your pants. We all want to get laid, right? I'll show you how to do it.

Most pickup manuals for hetero guys assume women need to be tricked into having sex. In fact, we're all tempted to do this from time to time—when we're insecure, we think the only way we'll get laid is if we manipulate others. But that's not my way—rather, I want you to become successful by being a better lover.

Similarly, a lot of sex advice for ladies is trivial: 'The secret to giving a great blow job,' for example. Okay, but how do we get there in the first place? I'll give you specific strategies for finding good partners.

No tricks. No secrets. We all need to understand each other.

Nowadays, thanks to the lessons I've learned, I'm having the time of my life. I pursue whomever I want, making new sexy friends with confidence. I love the sex I'm having… and my partners feel good too. For me, casual sex isn't casual—it's life-changing. Every time I connect with someone new, I'm mastering the art of the hook up.

Hook ups should be fun. They should be rewarding. They should leave yourself—and everyone else—feeling good. Let's get started on making that happen.

PART I

DON'T FORGET YOUR PANTS

Earl Burlingame, Lord of Mildenhall, awoke to a knocking on his chamber door. His elderly manservant entered, bearing a scrap of parchment.

'What is the meaning of this?' demanded the Earl. The staff of the castle were under strict instructions not to disturb him before luncheon.

'M'lord, a message has arrived. Apparently, a dragon has abducted your neighbour, Lady Myerscough.'

'Myerscough, eh?' The Earl snatched the paper from the servant's hand. He scanned the delicate script, written in haste and slightly scorched. The lady was beautiful, but she had yet to take an interest in him. Finally, a chance to prove himself!

'Fetch my horse!' the Earl said.

His chain mail and battle sword hung on the wall beside his bed. He fastened the buckles of the armour and slung the sword onto his back. Then he strode from the room.

Saddled on his charger, the Earl rode across the yard to the castle drawbridge. As was proper, his servants had gathered to see him off. But something about their demeanour puzzled him—where were the proud glances and respectful silence he had expected? Rather, there were mutterings. From the back of the room, someone chuckled.

His manservant shuffled forward. 'My lord-' he said.

'What is it?' the Earl snapped.

'My lord, you're not wearing any pants.'

With a sense of horror, Earl Burlingame realised that the old man spoke the truth.

Rushing out to hook up without preparing yourself is like trying to fight a dragon without pants on. You're exposed, you're at risk of injury, you look silly... and everyone knows it.

When I was younger, I hooked up with my friends, with my workmates, with folks I met at nightclubs, with people I met online... if you can imagine a way of picking up, I've probably done it. If experience equalled wisdom, I should have been wise well beyond my twenty-something years.

Except I wasn't. I lacked social skills, empathy, and sexual knowledge. I did whatever felt right with little consideration for the consequences. As I said previously, none of us are born knowing how to have good sex—we simply do our best, hoping nobody else notices we're winging it. I was no different.

What saved me? It wasn't learning some secret sexual technique. Rather, it was understanding my insecurities and negative attitudes about sex. Once I'd gained some confidence in myself, building my sex skills became much more straightforward.

Getting your head straight before seeking sex is an essential first step, a jumping-off point for positive encounters. If you don't do this stuff, you may find that the hands-on strategies we cover later in this book fall flat, because you don't feel safe or confident. When our heads aren't in the right place, the people we're trying to impress often pick up on that vibe—and no manner of fancy swordplay can save you, if you're not mentally equipped in the first place.

Part I will prepare you for your journey towards better hook ups. Together, we'll work out what you need. I'll show you ways to strengthen your confidence and create psychological safety.

Don't skip this stuff. Exploring the adventurous world of hook ups without knowing yourself first is like walking into the wilderness with no clothes: it won't end well. I want you to venture forth bravely with a map, some survival skills… and pants. Always remember the pants. Even if they end up on someone else's bedroom floor.

CHAPTER 1

AN INTRODUCTION TO HOOK UPS

Welcome to the Twenty-First Century! We're evolving faster than ever before and discovering incredible new ways to have sex. The popularity of online dating means people are stepping out of their comfort zones, finding partners outside their social circles, and trying new things in the bedroom.

Enter the hook up: a short-term sexual interaction that doesn't involve romance or long-term commitment.

When I first picked up guys, I assumed 'hook up' meant the same thing as 'one-night stand.' I had a 'drive-through' scenario going on: I'd get in my car, head over to my local nightclub, hang out on the dance floor for a while, pick up a hottie, and drive them back to my place. They usually slept over, and in the morning, I'd see them gently out the front door.

As I progressed further in my explorations, I discovered other ways to hook up. My friends often shagged their other friends. Sometimes, my mates dated more than one person at a time. We considered this sort of sexual behaviour wild in the noughties, but it's common nowadays among folks who want more options than 'married, forever' and have the apps to find like-minded partners.

untypical ways to hook up

> **HOOK-UP:** Sex (or sexy stuff) that isn't part of a romantic relationship.

To me, a hook up is neither romantic relationship nor long-term commitment. It's a sexual interaction that requires less time and emotional investment than a loving partnership.

This chapter covers hook up basics: what sorts of encounters qualify? Why do we do them? What can you get out of them? The answers might seem obvious, but it's not as straightforward as you think. Unpacking this stuff leads to some interesting places… and, ultimately, to a better knowledge of yourself.

WHAT DO YOU REALLY NEED?

Well, duh. Sex, right? Not so fast. Sex is never simple, and often there's a lot more to it than getting off.

Here's a story about my first day on the job as a sex worker. Most people outside the sex industry think the job is just about swapping sex for money. I thought so too when I started; I assumed I'd be meeting creepy, unattractive guys who couldn't get laid the regular way.

Then I met Gary.

Gary was my first ever escort client. He works as a manager for a courier company. Gary loves his footy and would be great with a pair of tongs at your family barbecue. Well, except that like the drummer from Def Leppard, Gary only has one arm. He was born with a congenital birth defect—one normal right arm, and one tiny stump growing out of his left shoulder. When Gary takes his shirt off, he looks like a mutant from Total Recall (luckily, he has a sense of humour about it, which is why I feel okay making that joke).

When Gary arrived on the scene, I assumed he just wanted sex. I hadn't met a one-armed man before, and I assumed seeing a sex worker was the only way he ever got laid.

This assumption was wrong. Sorry, Gary.

When I took him into the bedroom, I expected him to leap on me, sex-crazed and ravenous. But that's not what happened. We didn't have intercourse at all; instead, he spent an hour—an expensive hour—using his considerable manual skills to get me off. Gary devoted his entire session to pleasuring me; it was totally unexpected (and it took the whole hour, because I'm a tough case! Sorry, Gary.)

Near the end of the appointment, he told me how his ex-wife had lost interest in sex after the birth of their children. Gary loves making women happy and prefers pleasuring his partners over having conventional intercourse.

Gary taught me that people seek sex for surprising reasons. Since then, most of my clients have confirmed that sex means more to them than just

people are looking for different things in hook-up culture

the act itself. Although my work sometimes involves a good shag, it's often also about talking, cuddling, feeling appreciated, or trying new things.

Outside sex work, things are no different—we all have a variety of motivations for hooking up. Sometimes we don't like to admit our other needs, because we think casual sex is shallow. There's this idea that there are only two ways of being intimate with people outside your family:

1. The 'madly in love' option—reserved for long-term, committed partners.
2. The 'just sex' option—no feelings, no complications.

We often place non-traditional relationships in the 'no feelings, just sex' category. But feelings can, and do, get involved during casual sex.

In 2012 I went to the Eclipse Festival in Queensland—a week-long gathering to celebrate a rare Australian solar eclipse. Thousands of people came from all over the country; we camped under the stars and danced every night until the sun came up. One evening I found myself next to a super-hot, intelligent guy. He was an anaesthetist from Sydney in his ordinary life, but here he was a dust-covered, mysterious creature dancing shirtless under the full moon. We hung out all evening, and then I went back to his tent and we made sweaty, dusty love.

Afterwards, we spent hours talking about our lives back home. He spoke with a touching honesty about escaping the city grind. Our intimate sharing of feelings was the best part of the whole encounter, but it wouldn't have happened without physical connection. I never saw him again, but that moment of emotion was no less beautiful for being shared with a stranger. For me, our hook up was about the intimacy, not the intercourse. Sex was just the way we established enough trust to open up to each other.

COMMON BENEFITS OF SEX

- **Romance** (feelings of love, chemical bonding.)
- **Friendship** (shared activities, interests and confidences.)
- **Sexual touch** (involving genitals, orgasms, etc.)
- **Physical touch** (cuddles, massages, hand holding, spooning.)
- **Emotional intimacy** (sharing feelings.)
- **Emotional support** (being listened to, asking for and receiving advice.)
- **Social company** (having someone to take to the movies, etc.)

So many options! It's much more complicated than 'not serious, no feelings.'

REASONS I HOOK UP

- **To relieve sexual tension**. Everyone gets horny, right? When I catch myself watching Magic Mike one too many times, I know it's time to get off the couch and find a date. This might sound a little surprising if you've been raised to think women don't have high libidos. More on that later—but for now, let me just say that ladies are often just as interested in sex as any other gender. If you've been told none of us enjoy it, someone's been fibbing to you.

- **To create emotional bonds**. Sex breaks down emotional barriers. I love feeling close to my partner, even if we're not in a romantic relationship. Again, common gender stereotypes might mean this sounds weird to you. Mainstream culture often shames men for having feelings; you might assume that connection is a 'chick thing.' But guys enjoy emotional intimacy too!

- **To play and experiment**. Everyone is into different 'play' in the bedroom. When I hook up with a variety of people, I can experiment with positions, toys, kinks, and ways of pleasing my partners.

- **Because meeting new people (and seeing them naked) is interesting**. It's a great way to learn about human beings—and because we're all different, it never gets boring!

- **To practise my skills.** Nothing gets better without practice! That goes for sex skills and people skills. Hooking up requires me to work on both.

WHY MY FRIENDS HOOK UP

- 'It keeps me going between serious relationships.'
- 'I have sex to blow off steam when I'm stressed.'
- 'I'm shy around other people, and this is my way to improve before I get a girlfriend.'
- 'I enjoy finding people I click with sexually, and then maybe think about turning it into a relationship after a while.'
- I don't have time for a regular partner, but I still want to get laid sometimes.'

There are also reasons for casual sex we sometimes don't want to admit, even to ourselves. These are the less noble motivations that would make us seem self-indulgent if we revealed them in polite company. Luckily, you're not in polite company now, so here they are.

TO FEEL SEXY

We love being told we're sexy, but there's something particularly honest about a partner showing their sincerity via physical affection. We all have something about our bodies we wish we could change; fucking someone helps remind us that these imperfections don't matter. My work as an escort has taught me that everyone finds different physical appearances attractive; I've lost count of the times a guy has told me 'I love your butt!' or 'Your belly is awesome!' It's a great ego boost.

Warning: if your sexual partners are complimentary and you still feel bad about yourself, it might be a good idea to work on that issue on your own time. If you hate your own body, it will be difficult for anyone else to convince you otherwise. I enjoy the praise when I receive it, but also don't rely too much on the opinions of others. Seeing myself as sexy is equally important.

WANTING TO BRAG ABOUT IT AFTERWARDS

Feeling like a sexual champion is a total high. Bragging is discouraged in Aussie culture, because we don't want to look like we're egotistical, but I will admit that I often high-five my friends the day after I get laid.

Warning: the problem arises when we fixate on quantity over quality. When sex is just a way of getting social approval, you'll miss out on enjoying it, which defeats the point. If you find some balance—other life pursuits and character traits that show what an awesome human you are—then a bit of celebrating is fine.

ENJOYING THE CHASE

I'm a moderately attractive thirty-something woman, and I love fucking twenty-five-year-olds. It's exciting, like going on 'sexual conquest' safari. I enjoy seducing people—this is the stuff of romance novels (and porn movies).

Warning: Unfortunately, this game can take a dark turn. If you get too caught up in the chase, you may feel tempted to pressure your crush into having sex with you. Even the word 'conquest' suggests overpowering someone, right? That's not cool. When we think of our partners as unwilling participants, there's often the temptation to use pushy and underhanded tactics that fuck up the whole situation.

WANTING TO FEEL HAPPY

Sex releases happy chemicals, such as dopamine and serotonin, into our brains. We feel jazzed, euphoric, or even high, like a kid that's eaten lots of candy. Sex is a great pick-me-up and an effective way to bond with people you care about.

Warning: it's not a miracle cure. If you're unhappy, sex will not fix this—in fact, if you're feeling bad, sex can distract from the real issues. If hooking up feels empty for you, or makes you depressed, I'd recommend sorting yourself out with the help of a therapist.

Sometimes we're afraid to be honest about what we want... but focusing only on the sex might leave you wanting. Also, when we're not honest with people, they can tell... and that vibe can kill off your chances of getting laid.

Another common misconception is that we're not allowed to search for a particular interaction: that we're lucky to get anything, and we have to put up with it even if it's not exactly right. This is especially true when opportunities are thin on the ground, because nobody wants to miss out. To be clear, I'm not saying you should limit yourself just because someone doesn't meet all your needs—if you want to go for it, then go for it. But it's good to be clear on your needs so that, if you pursue someone, you'll have a realistic idea of how rewarding the experience is likely to be.

Your needs are valid. Own them and own up to them, because knowing what makes you happy is crucial.

YOUR HOOK-UP OPTIONS EXPLAINED

There are many ways to connect with partners, and not all are of the pash-and-dash variety. Here are a few options.

ONE-NIGHT STAND

A scenario in which you have sex with someone and then never see them again. In the movies it's done as an overnighter: when the hero/heroine wakes up in the morning, they find that their partner has quietly dressed and left without saying a word. But it happens other ways too—fuck and leave, sleep over and breakfast the next day, encounter at a sex club… or even a fling with a stranger in your best friend's bedroom during a party.

My favourite one-night stand took place while I was on vacation. My partner was an ex-special-forces soldier from the USA. He was charming, thoughtful and open about his experiences. I couldn't decide which was better: the sex, or the conversation!

FRIEND WITH BENEFITS (FWB)

Someone you spend time with and whose company you enjoy, but who you also have sex with. This is the hook up variety most likely to evolve into a long-term relationship. However, many people do fuck their friends, successfully and enjoyably, without long-term romantic attachment.

NO STRINGS ATTACHED (NSA)

Shorthand for 'sex without obligation'. I don't like this term because it suggests 'sex without responsibility,' and I believe we all have a responsibility to respect and care for the people we sleep with. But, like it or not, NSA is a thing people do.

FUCK BUDDY

Someone who, like an FWB, is around on an ongoing basis. In this relationship, it's more about the sex than the friendship: you are friends with
this person because you both want to bang each other.

I met one of my most enduring fuck buddies during a night of dancing at
a club in Sydney. I'd been checking out this guy across the dance floor—he
had an eye-catching, eight-inch mohawk. His best friend came over to
chat me up, and when I confessed my interest in the other guy the friend
promptly introduced us; best wingman ever!

We wound up sleeping together for years. Because we hung out at the
same club, we'd often go home together at the end of the night. We knew
we weren't a good romantic match, but the sex was great. My fuck buddy
is now married to an amazing woman, and they're expecting their first
child—but I still receive messages from him now and then saying, 'Hey,
remember the fun we had? I'm so glad we did that.'

BOOTY CALL

Someone who is available at short notice for sex (often at odd hours). I don't
like booty calls; I enjoy sleeping, so being woken up makes me bad-tem-
pered. But your mileage may vary.

PLAY PARTNER

A person you play with, in some sexual manner. I use this term to describe
the folks I do kink stuff with, which doesn't always include actual sexual
intercourse. It's a nice term for lovers too, because 'play' sounds like fun,
and good sex should be fun!

LOVER

You might think, 'Wait, what? We're not supposed to have feelings for our hook ups, what's all this about love and shit?' If you read on, you'll discover that I believe emotions have a place in every hook up, no matter how brief. So, for me, a lover is someone I care for and see regularly even though I don't intend to have a long-term or full-time relationship with them. It's hard to manage the feelings around a lover-type relationship, but they can be very rewarding.

Life is busy for me right now; I don't have time for a full-time partnership. I do, however, have some people I love spending time with—whether it's sex, or just watching movies and sharing a glass of wine. Recently, I caught the Winter flu, and they contacted me daily to see if I needed anything; it was almost like being cared for by a romantic partner!

These definitions are starting points, but words mean different things to different people. Use your own words, if you prefer. When the person you're fucking says, 'What are we doing here, exactly?' it's good to know your options.

Next, we find out whether you're ready.

ARE HOOK UPS RIGHT FOR YOU?

Is this something you're down for? It's important to be honest with yourself, because hook ups aren't for everyone, and that's okay. Before you go charging into the wilderness, you need to make sure you're cut out for the journey.

Sometimes I don't feel like getting sexy with strangers. Often, it's because I'm looking for a romantic relationship, so I avoid casual dating until I find the right person. Sometimes I'm depressed and can't endure being unmatched on Tinder. Sometimes I'm too busy to arrange hook ups—while writing this book, for example.

There are lots of legit reasons that people don't hook up, including:

- **They prefer to be in a romantic relationship** with the person they're fucking.
- **They've made a choice** not to have sex outside a committed relationship, or outside marriage.
- **They aren't into sex at all,** or barely (this is what we call asexual. Often these folks will find other ways to connect with their partners that don't involve sex).
- **They're demisexual**—they need to form an emotional bond with someone before they feel sexually attracted.
- **They feel physically or emotionally unsafe** dating new people.
- **Life circumstances make it difficult for them**, e.g., being in jail, disability (although lots of people with disabilities lead active sex lives) or chronic illness.
- **They 'just don't feel like it, okay?!'**

What has your experience been so far? If you've hooked up in the past, did you enjoy it? Do you feel good about the sex you've had, or does it make you feel ashamed? All the above hints at how positively you feel about sex.

How much do you value yourself as a person? Our self-esteem can be fragile, and if you're feeling down, then getting vulnerable with strangers might be difficult. If you find rejection challenging, your self-esteem can take a real beating. Consider doing some work on yourself (via counselling or self-help) before you risk your mental health.

Lastly, how much room do you have in your life for hook ups right now? How much time and effort are you willing to devote to this? I'm not just talking about dates—I'm also referring to the time spent finding people, and the mental effort of managing every new situation. Hooking up is more of an investment than we realise when we first swipe on a dating app.

Of course, we all change, and trying something new is a great way to grow as a person. Maybe it's time to give it a go? But if there's a voice in your head saying 'Hell, no!' then I give you permission to put this book down and walk away. There's no shame in knowing what's right for you.

TOO LONG; DIDN'T READ (TL;DR)

- Sex isn't just 'romance' versus 'no feelings'—there's a lot of middle ground.
- Hook ups come in many varieties (and acronyms). It's not just about one-night stands.
- People hook up for different reasons (not just for sex).
- Get your head straight before you try it—is casual sex for you? There's no shame in saying no!
- Identify your needs to maximise your satisfaction.

Now you know the possibilities, it's almost time to get things happening… but first, we look at some mental strategies to keep you safe during your adventures.

CHAPTER 2

YOUR PROTECTIVE EQUIPMENT

This chapter is about your protective gear—and I'm not talking about helmets and chain mail. I mean support and self-care. Both are an essential part of staying emotionally safe on your hook-up journey.

When we look for dates, we rarely consider our psychological safety. Our 'man up' culture means we often don't talk about our feelings. But even the roughest bloke has a sense of self-worth! No matter your gender, your self-esteem is important.

You might think it's silly to talk about safety. It makes it sound as though things will go wrong.

Well, I hate to break it to you, but things will definitely go wrong.

Sex is a risky activity. Mishaps are inevitable: rejections, disrespect, feeling scared, or fucking up. Your protective equipment helps get you through… and will make you feel stronger next time.

I recently helped a friend called Karl shoot some photos for his online dating profile. He's the kind of dude who cracks the first joke at a party, but also surprises you with thoughtful insights on life—a keeper, basically. As we were wandering the laneways of Fitzroy, he told me the story of his fling with pickup artistry.

Pickup artists (PUAs) are folks (usually guys) who strategise the process of getting laid. It's about styling your image, learning conversation starters, or sometimes confidence-boosting techniques. I understand why guys go for it—in the stressful world of dating, who doesn't want short cuts? But many of these tricks piss women off and leave guys feeling awkward.

Karl got carried away with this stuff. He practised 'day game', which is when you approach women on the street to ask for dates. Most of the women he approached turned him down, which didn't surprise me. I mean, would you enjoy being interrupted by a stranger while you're on your way to work?

The experience scarred him. 'I can't approach women in public at all now, even if it's at a club or a pub,' he told me. 'Getting rejected so often totally crushed me. Now, when I want to ask someone out, all I can think of is the fifty or sixty women who said no.'

Rejection—although a fact of life—has real consequences for our self-esteem. Karl didn't consider the effect it would have on his psyche, and he paid the price. If only he'd stopped to discuss the idea with a friend first, they might have discouraged him. Or perhaps if he'd been more aware of his emotions, he would have noticed how bad he was feeling and called the whole thing off.

This chapter explains three crucial techniques for protecting yourself: support, self-care, and listening to your fear. Getting this right is the mental equivalent of having steel-plate armour and a good first-aid kit. It's a big, bad world out there—so pack the psychological essentials before you get started.

HOW TO GET SUPPORT FROM OTHERS

Everyone needs support—someone they can take their problems to when they're stuck. We're not designed to be lone wolves all the time. Even a lone wolf returns to the pack!

Support is all about the people who help you: a sympathetic ear, some helpful advice, a cup of tea. It may mean getting a lift back from the pub at two in the morning, or an offer to crash on someone's couch when you don't want to be alone.

Women are often good at support—we love our coffee-and-gossip sessions. But support isn't restricted to any one gender. Lots of folks are down for a good chat. Your mates might offer support in a variety of ways—if they're not up for a deep-and-meaningful convo, they could still give you a hug or shout you a beer. Family can also be an option, depending on how open you are with your siblings or parents.

In bad times, having unsupportive friends becomes a liability. If they think it's weak to admit you've had a bad day, or don't pay attention when you're in trouble, consider investing in better people. I know this is easier said than done—it's not just a matter of taking them back to the shop for an exchange! But it's worth putting some effort into making friends with the people that will stick by you in your darkest times, because we all need help occasionally. Don't be caught short.

If you don't have access to adequate support from friends and family, there are still options. A counsellor is great, if you have the cash. Therapy isn't always about seeing a professional to fix a problem—sometimes it's just a great way to get something off your chest. When seeking a mental health pro, make sure you find someone who won't judge you for your casual sex adventures.

If you're a bloke, check out 'means sheds' and 'men's circles' in your area—these organisations have events where men can get together and talk in a supportive space. These sorts of community groups exist for people of all genders—try googling 'support groups.'

If you're in immediate trouble, I recommend crisis lines such as Lifeline (13 11 14 in Australia) and MensLine (1300 78 99 78).

INFORMAL SUPPORTS
- **Friends**—hopefully sex-positive and supportive ones… if they aren't, ditch them and find some new ones, pronto!
- **Workmates**—depending on the relationship you have with them and whether it's appropriate to talk about what you get up to on the weekend.
- **Family**—maybe… your mum might not want to know every detail of your sex life, but you may still be able to ask for a hug or a cup of tea.
- **Discussion boards and online groups** such as you can find on social media.

FORMAL SUPPORTS
- **Counsellors and psychologists**—make sure they're sex-positive.
- **Men's/women's/special interest groups**—as above! You want people who make you a better person, not drag you down or shame you.
- Crisis helplines—such as Lifeline or MensLine.

My best support is my close friend Alexandra. We call each other whenever we need to talk—not just on sad days, but also for celebrations. Whether I've just been dumped, or I've returned from a fun escort booking, I know she'll listen.

Like a station full of firefighters, your supports need to be primed before you run into trouble. When shit has already gone wrong, it's often too late. Make the friends you can, sound out your mates to make sure they'll stand by you, or find alternatives. Do it before you get into trouble, so you won't have any delays getting help when you need it.

HOW TO BE A SELF-CARE CHAMPION

Self-care is a solitary pursuit. Basically, it's anything you do to keep yourself in good mental and physical shape. The stronger and healthier you feel, the safer it is to experiment with hook ups.

This is basic stuff. Self-care doesn't have to be about getting emotional. It can be something small; getting enough sleep or drinking more water. It can also mean making important life decisions, such as cutting off contact with a friend who mistreats you or quitting a job that makes you miserable.

Sometimes we don't call it self-care. Sometimes we call it 'chucking a sickie', 'chilling out', or 'checking out for a while.' Often, we do it without even thinking about it. We take a long drive, watch Netflix for eight hours straight, or treat ourselves to a fancy lunch.

BASIC SELF-CARE
- Eating something healthy, drinking some water, and taking a nap.

- Giving yourself permission to take it easy for the day.
- Booking an appointment to see your counsellor.
- Going to your dad's place for a chat.
- Taking a long walk, or a long drive.
- Writing your feelings down in a journal (or on the back of your shopping receipt, whatever works).

Choose a strategy that works for you. When I feel terrible, I lock myself in my apartment, order takeaway, and spend the day in bed with a good book. Recently, after breaking up with a lover, I built a blanket fort in my bedroom and hid in it! Being alone to think things over always helps me feel better.

Self-care is your responsibility. If you don't look after yourself, nobody else is going to do it for you. What do you do to feel better when things don't work out with someone you really like, or you're worried about your next date? Make a mental list and stash it in your self-care toolkit. As with support, this stuff works better when you plan. You don't want to get stuck for ideas when you've had a bad day.

FEAR IS YOUR FRIEND

I have a friend who went to a sex party. His name is Zac.

Zac went to the party with the goal of getting laid. There were so many opportunities there—people of all types and personalities, eager to make his acquaintance! Sounds perfect, right? Alas, Zac fucked it up.

He'd never been to a sex party before and was, understandably, anxious. Before he went, he had several drinks to drown his fear. 'I wanted to get over the nerves,' he told me, 'but I got so wasted that I ended up doing all this shit I didn't want to do. I made out with people I wasn't attracted to. I did more sex stuff than I had planned, and I felt bad the next day. Everyone there saw me carrying on like a drunk dickhead.' He felt ashamed of himself, and he never went back.

Sometimes, when we feel scared, we try to push through it. We're told that courage means ignoring our fears—even the phrase 'step out of your comfort zone' suggests we need feel uncomfortable in order to succeed.

It's great to challenge yourself. But you need to know *how far to step out.*

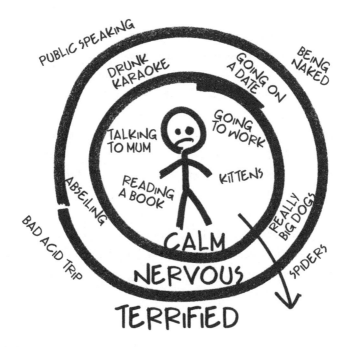

We all have different tolerances for different challenges. As in the diagram, you might love catching up with friends, hate exams, and completely avoid public speaking. Or perhaps speeches are okay, but getting into a fist fight is too much? It depends on you.

There's a principle called 'finding the resilient edge of resistance': going out of your comfort zone just a little, then returning to safety afterwards. Think of it as expanding your comfort zone... it's a gradual stretch of what feels safe, not a giant leap into danger.

As you stretch your idea of what's possible, fear is an essential tool. Fear is the warning light of the soul—it exists to let us know when we're in danger. When we take risks, our bodies release adrenaline and cortisol to prepare us to respond to a potentially dangerous situation. Like the fuel light on our car dashboards (the one I ignore until I run out of petrol on the M-80), fear gives you information you can use.

Listen to your fear. It might say 'be careful.' It might say, 'watch out, danger coming!' Or it might be a sign you're not yet ready to attempt a task. Don't bury your feelings under bravado or denial. The more you tune in to your fear, the better you can use it to navigate.

In escorting, we often say, 'trust your gut'. If a situation doesn't feel right, it probably isn't. When I feel, deep down, that something is wrong—even if I can't put my finger on why—I walk away. The risk of offending someone is much less important than protecting my safety!

You can back off and try again later, but if you ignore your fear and push ahead, you're cutting yourself off from something that's designed to protect you. And as we've discussed, short-term-dating is full of mishaps. It's much safer to go at a pace that feels right for you.

TOO LONG; DIDN'T READ (TL;DR)

- Hook ups will inevitably get you down at some stage—that's the nature of the game.
- Get some support and self-care ideas together before the bad stuff happens.

- Fear is your friend—use it to judge when you're moving out of your depth.

Hopefully, you'll be feeling safer now, before you leave the castle gates. It's time to get out of our own heads and into everyone else's… the next chapter uncovers the bullshit assumptions we all make about sex that could prevent you getting laid.

CHAPTER 3

NORMAL IS BULLSHIT

Sometimes our assumptions can really fuck things up.

I once picked up a hot guy during a night out. He was younger than me, charming and full of drunk bravado. We went back to my place, had sex, and fell asleep, with absolutely no discussion of our expectations.

When we woke the next day, he offered to give me his number. I said, 'no way,' laughed at him, and kicked him out of my apartment. I remember how hurt he looked as I slammed the front door in his face. It was a shitty way to treat another human being—sure, I didn't owe him anything, but perhaps a 'thank you' would have been kinder? I sometimes wonder how that experience affected him; perhaps it made him afraid to attempt one-night stands in the future, or perhaps he now treats his partners as selfishly as I did. I'll never know.

I treated that guy as disposable because I assumed that he was only interested in sex, not an ongoing relationship. And I wasn't honest about wanting a one-night stand, because I didn't realise that honesty was an option.

My asshole behaviour resulted from the weird ideas about sex I learned growing up. I was burdened with three flawed ideas:

1. If you're not doing sex the same way as everyone else, there's something wrong with you.
2. Guys always act one way, and girls always act a different way.
3. Sex is something embarrassing that we shouldn't talk about.

Before you can have a great hook up, you need to ditch the bullshit. This includes any stereotypical assumptions about men and women and any lingering feelings of shame about getting laid. Above all, it means giving up on your fear of being different… because there's no such thing as normal. This chapter will unpick some common misconceptions about sex and dating that might be holding you back.

Don't let assumptions blind you—open your eyes.

WHAT'S WRONG WITH BEING NORMAL?

There's nothing wrong with being normal. It's just that, when it comes to sex, there's really no such thing.

When I was nineteen, I worried my sexual fantasies were weird. I used to think about getting tied up by people or having sex with several guys at once—hot masturbatory material, I can tell you! But I didn't tell my friends. I instinctively knew that if I admitted to my fantasies, they'd call me a pervert. Fast-forward a decade, and I'm part of a social circle of kinky people who love adventurous sex. It's the new normal for everyone I hang out with. To them, the word 'deviant' is a compliment.

When researcher Alfred Kinsey published the *Kinsey Reports* in 1948 and 1953, he challenged the idea that there is any such thing as normal sex. His ground-breaking surveys studied human behaviour such as sexual orientation, kinks, and how much sex people were having. He expected that everyone would be roughly the same, with a few folks on the fringes. Instead, he discovered that people were getting into a HUGE variety of sexual situations. The sexual behaviours he discovered were so diverse that he struggled to find anyone typical at all. Turns out, people get up to interesting things when nobody is watching!

Normal is a made-up idea. It's a lot of 'should' and not much info about how people really behave. Sexual culture changes over time; what your parents' generation thought was deviant—oral sex, for example—is now commonplace. Since opinions change, how can we trust anyone to tell us what's acceptable? What really matters is that you treat yourself and your dates with respect.

Social norms are like being part of a school of fish—nobody knows where we're going, because we're following others. Safety in numbers, right? If you swim against the stream, some folks get mighty upset. To them, breaking the rules is scary… and if they see you getting away with it, they feel threatened.

Sometimes it's the opposite problem: we feel judged for not being sexually adventurous. When other people act proud of themselves for being kinky, or having lots of sexual partners, they're getting sucked into the same myth—that there's a normal standard. Only difference is, they think they're better for deviating from it.

I don't think it matters what you're into, how much sex you have, or who you have it with. Whether you stick with missionary position or wear a leather gimp mask to bed, you have a right to feel good. I believe we should work hard at being ourselves, whatever that means... normal be damned.

STEREOTYPES & OTHER IMAGINARY BEASTS

Modern culture teaches us a lot of 'girl/guy' rules—basically, the way people are supposed to act based on their genitals. I know some of you might be thinking, 'stereotypes are there for a reason' and they sure are! Stereotypes exist because we're lazy—we like to generalise about the ways males and females are different, instead of admitting that people of all genders are often similar.

> **STEREOTYPE:** A widely-held (but often bullshit) idea about a particular type of person.

Stereotypes are problematic beasts. They give rise to assumptions... and, as my dad says, 'When you assume you make an ass of u and me.' People never fit perfectly into the roles we assign for them. Men don't always behave the way we expect, and neither do women—we're individuals. Here are some examples of stereotypes that can fuck up your hook-up attempts.

MYTH #1: WOMEN DON'T ENJOY SEX
Women can, and do, enjoy sex.

This is going to sound obvious to a lot of ladies—I bet you're all sniggering and muttering, 'Thanks, Captain Obvious.' But it's not obvious to everyone. Mostly, I'm writing this for my friend Robert.

Robert is about forty years old. When he was a teenager, he attended an all-boys Catholic school, and their sex education was terrible. The sex-ed class was run by one of the priests, who assured the boys that women simply don't enjoy sex. Robert says, 'He basically drew this graph on the blackboard, to show the level of pleasure during a sexual encounter. And for women, it was just a flat line.'

As he grew into adulthood, Robert worried that his girlfriends hated intercourse. 'I assumed that if a partner asked for sex, she was only doing it to make me happy. It made me ashamed of my own sexual urges—I felt that just by wanting to do this stuff, I was hurting someone.'

The belief that women don't like sex creates two huge problems:

1. Some straight guys assume that since women don't like physical intimacy, the only way to get laid is to trick, manipulate, or force them into it. This is how sexual assault happens, people! But aside from coercion, it also results in bad sex. I mean, if a bloke thinks his partner hates it, he's not going to bother trying to make her orgasm, is he?

2. People (of all genders) think that women who do enjoy sex are deviant, and that there's something wrong with them. If you've ever had a female partner who can't tell you what she wants, fear of judgement could be the issue. We're so used to being criticised that we're often afraid to admit we have sex at all. My female friends and I have tons of sex; we just don't tell strangers, because we don't want to be called 'nymphos'. Then my hetero guy friends come to me and complain, 'Where are all the women who like sex?'

This myth is less pervasive now we have online dating apps. Lots of my single female friends are hooking up, even if only between relationships.

Women have sex drives too! Like guys, their needs range from low, to average, to sex-obsessed; you can't be sure, unless you ask.

MYTH #2: GUYS WANT SEX, GIRLS WANT ROMANCE.

As the story goes, guys are only after one thing—they want to have sex with as many people as possible. Males have higher sex drives, science says so! (It doesn't, actually—according to many experts, there's a lot of variation in sex drive for all genders.) It's often assumed that guys want to shag as many women as possible, to spread their genes around. On the other hand, girls are supposed to want love, marriage and babies… they aren't supposed to be interested in sex, unless it helps them lure a partner into a committed relationship. Charles Darwin popularised this attitude during Victorian Times, and it seems to have stuck around. But research has since shown us that not all male mammals fuck indiscriminately, and not all females stick with one partner. Sex and commitment aren't exclusive to one gender.

This stereotype encourages men to trick women into sex. It creates emotional anxiety, because guys fear being tricked into commitment. Those who do want a long-term relationship are often disregarded, because the ladies don't take them seriously. And labelling all women lovebirds means we often feel ashamed to seek out sex.

MYTH #3: GUYS SHOULD BE SEXUALLY EXPERIENCED AND AGGRESSIVE… GIRLS SHOULD BE INEXPERIENCED AND PASSIVE.

Hey, guys—do you feel as though you always have to make the first move? Does letting someone else take control seem un-masculine? Like fixing cars, sex is something blokes are supposed to be experts at, even if they've never touched an engine—uh, I mean a breast—in their lives.

This is part of what's called 'toxic masculinity', the way society pressures men to fit into a specific role. Men are expected to be strong, confident, have massive dicks, and demonstrate never-ending sexual stamina. They're expected to be in control of the sexual interaction, and never fuck up, otherwise they're considered losers. The problem is, no one person can tick all those boxes. We all have bad days when we're not confident, and our bodies don't do what we want. Not all men want to be dominant in bed. Shaming guys for not fitting the stereotype is a load of bullshit, and it makes some men deeply unhappy.

A lot of guys get annoyed with the phrase 'toxic masculinity' because they think their own masculinity is being criticised. But what I'm talking about here is—in my opinion—a cultural conspiracy to make men miserable, by telling them they're never going to measure up. Don't fall for it; you're allowed to be your own flawed, human self.

The stereotype women are supposed to live up to is just as bad. We're lumped with the role of being the passive partner who is available for the sexual pleasure of others but not for her own. We continually feel as though we must look attractive and make the people around us happy. If we admit to enjoying sex ourselves, we're called sluts. If we're too assertive, we're considered scary. This is called 'toxic femininity'. Again, this doesn't mean all femininity is toxic... but pressure to be the perfect woman sure is!

Expecting guys to act like sexual superstars is only setting them up for failure. And shaming women for being sexually experienced means none of us will own up to liking sex, for fear of being treated badly.

MYTH #4: GUYS ARE SEXUAL PREDATORS, AND WOMEN ARE VICTIMS.

Data tells us that when it comes to sexual assault, most perpetrators are men and most victims are women. So, when I talk about safety in this book, it's mostly there for the benefit of femme folk—it's an accepted fact that men are more likely to do the attacking.

But it's hurtful and self-defeating to say that all men are predators and all women are victims. It makes some guys think, 'Treating women badly is normal, so why try to be nice?' It gives the bad guys an excuse to be assholes, because everyone already thinks they're sex offenders. And how about the good guys? Many men feel a deep shame around their own sexual desires, since they've been told that having desires at all means they're potential rapists. This means they have trouble talking about sex, and the communication that's needed for safe hook ups goes right out the window.

This stereotype also often allows women to forget that they do have power when it comes to a sexual exchange. Not only do we need to communicate with our partners, we also need to consider their rights. Consent violations happen to people of all genders; women can and sometimes do hurt others, emotionally or physically. Everyone has a responsibility to care for the person they're fucking.

Here are some examples of people I know, who don't fit the stereotypes.

- A beautiful lady friend of mine goes right up to guys she likes in bars and says, 'are you interested in getting laid?' Her potential partners are so weirded-out by a lady making the first move that they usually run away.

- Another friend who picks up gay guys has trouble finding a loving, long-term relationship, because their sexual partners assume that they're only interested in one-night stands.

- I once had a boyfriend who was uncomfortable with the fact that I was more sexually experienced than he. In his mind, it was always the guy who should know more—even though it made absolutely no difference to the quality of our sex life. His hang-ups meant that our relationship didn't last.

People don't fit neatly into boxes. If you start making assumptions about how men or women act, it means you can't see the person standing in front of you for who they are.

SEX-NEGATIVITY: THE ENEMY OF GOOD SEX

Picture this scene: myself and a co-worker during a shift in our local supermarket. I was employed as a shelf-stacker (not my favourite job in the world, but whatever.) We were huddled behind the shelves, having a good old gossip.

Co-worker (giggling): I heard you made out with Barry at the work Christmas party last night! You go, girl!

Me: Yeah, he was pretty good in bed too.

Co-worker (horrified): Oh, my god, you had SEX with him? Why did you do that?

Me: Wait, what?

Sex-negativity is the feeling that sex is inherently bad and shameful: something we should be guilty about. It's not always logical. Sex-negativity creates an invisible line you're not supposed to cross; like my workmate at the supermarket, people will often approve of one thing but condemn you for another.

SEX-NEGATIVITY: A judgement (or feeling) that sex is dirty, dangerous, or deviant.

Sex-negativity is handed down to us like an heirloom… and, like your nanna's antique tea set, it's very hard to get rid of. We pick it up at a young age from parents, teachers, and religious leaders. Every little comment—'sex is gross' or 'masturbation is unhealthy'—adds more darkness to our souls. By the time we get old enough to start having sexual feelings, we've already been well-trained to feel ashamed of our desires.

EXAMPLES OF SEX-NEGATIVITY
- When your dad criticises women on the street for their short skirts, saying they look like sluts.
- When your pastor says masturbation is a sin.
- When someone on TV says that porn stars must have been abused as kids.
- When you ask your parents where babies come from, and they get all weird about it.
- When you have sex with your high school sweetheart, and your friends act scandalised.

- When your new boyfriend gets upset because you've slept with three people before him.
- When your friends call you a 'player,' because you like sex with more than one person

Sex is not bad for you. Lots of scientific studies have demonstrated that it's good for your immune system and your mental health. This applies whether it's with a long-term romantic partner, a hook up, or just with your own hand. Sex increases the testosterone levels of all genders—this results in sharper thinking, more muscle, and improved bone density. If you're training hard at the gym, don't forget to have some orgasms to improve your gainz!

What about sexually transmitted infections (STIs)? Someone said this to me once: 'Since you sleep with more people than me, you obviously have a higher risk of getting an STI. So, I'm not going to date you.' He thought he was being perfectly logical. In fact, he was perfectly wrong. Lowering STI risk is more about your safer sex practices than the number of people you fuck. Using condoms correctly makes a huge difference. You can take it from someone who hooks up a lot, both at work and in my personal life—it's not the numbers.

What about sexual violence, disrespectful behaviour, and people being assholes? Yeah, it happens, and it's not always avoidable. This kind of stuff often occurs because people think that sex is shameful, and therefore that it's okay to be nasty to people who do it. The more folks come around to the idea that sex is normal and natural, the less bad behaviour we'll have to deal with.

Isn't meaningless sex bad for you? There's this idea that sex outside relationships is destructive—that it will leave us lonely, used up, and sad. Well, the human body is an amazing thing—it can survive marathon sex sessions (my record is six hours). Sex is great for our immune systems and connecting with other humans makes our bodies produce dopamine and oxytocin, which is good for our mood. Anyway, who said casual sex is 'meaningless'? I've had deep, significant emotional experiences with my casual partners. The experience of meeting new people, learning to trust, and learning from others—that's not casual. That's what I call personal growth.

If we're open about our sexual behaviour (or if we get caught out) then the shit really hits the fan. We're often labelled immoral, slutty, or dirty. This is 'slut-shaming', the practice of hating on someone that has too much sex. In this context, too much sex' could mean any sex at all, from some folks' point of view. It's a bit like the speed you drive at on the road: we assume anyone who goes faster us is a reckless idiot, and anyone who goes slower than us is a bad driver. When it comes to sex, we often see people who have less than us as losers, and people who have more are sluts or players. It's a no-win situation.

SLUT SHAMING: Judging someone for having too much sex, the wrong sort of sex, or any sex at all.

My best friend Adele is, like me, a dedicated Tinder enthusiast. But she runs into trouble when she reveals to guys that she's not searching for a relationship. 'It's really weird,' she says, 'Even though the guys I match with are only looking to get laid, they act like there's something wrong with me for wanting sex. Double standards, much?'

Some of you might be thinking, 'Good guys don't do one-night stands.' I've heard that one before. It's framed as chivalry, but it's really sex-negativity in disguise. Some people think that treating partners badly is a normal part of casual sex, and the only way to avoid it is to avoid having sex at all. But it doesn't have to be that way. Respect and sex can coexist. It's entirely possible to hook up with someone, value them as a person, and treat them kindly.

HOW TO DEAL WITH SEX-NEGATIVITY

- **Refuse to play by the rules.** Refuse to be embarrassed about the sex you're having and tell the haters to fuck off. It takes a lot of practice, because being criticised often triggers our own sex shame. That little voice in your head that says, 'You're a terrible person!' is your inner sex-negativity. Keep shouting it down.

- **Be honest with yourself.** Question your attitudes about sex. Do you feel bad when you get laid? Do you judge other people for the sex they're having? Talk your feelings over with a friend or counsellor. The aim is to get to a place where sex feels normal, rather than naughty.

- **Turn off the projector.** Sometimes, when we feel bad, we try to offload those uncomfortable feelings onto others. Psychologists call this 'projecting.' It happens when you've got a crush on someone and you're convinced they have feelings for you, even though they haven't given any sign. But it also happens with sex-negativity—if you think sex is bad, you might sidestep the shame and instead blame the people you're fucking. For example: if you judge the women you sleep with but give yourself a free pass, then your projector needs to be switched off. Pronto.

- **Walk the talk.** If your friends criticise others for their sexual behaviour, tell them to quit it—or give them a copy of this book! Otherwise, those same friends might turn on you once they hear about all the hot hook-up sex you're having.

Sex-negativity is something other people put on us, and it's also something that we do to ourselves. It fucks up our sexual interactions, leads us to behave cruelly towards our partners, and robs us of the enjoyment we could be feeling.

In order to have better sex, we must stop thinking it's shameful. As long as you treat your hook ups with respect, you're not doing anything wrong.

TOO LONG; DIDN'T READ (TL;DR)

- The idea of 'normal' is bullshit—it's more important that you treat everyone respectfully.
- Stereotypes stop us from seeing the real person behind the assumptions.
- Sex-negativity is forced on us by our crappy, repressive culture. It's not good for you—drop it like a hot potato, if you can!
- Most of our negative assumptions about hook ups are wrong (or only right if you get sucked in by the lies.)

Congratulations—you've levelled up! You've learned about casual sex and equipped yourself with some powerful safety strategies. Forewarned and forearmed, we're ready to get physical. Now it's time to put our hands firmly on the steering wheel. Next up, Part II details the route to a good hook up.

PART II

KEEP YOUR HANDS ON THE WHEEL

Ever feel as though you're a passenger in your own sex life?

We often think of sex as a mysterious process beyond our control. 'I just got carried away!' we might exclaim, as though getting laid only happens once our animal instincts take over. Here's the problem: when we equate sex with losing control, we also lose control over the quality of our encounters.

In Part I we looked at what you think… in Part II we'll be discussing what you DO. Here are the skills you can use to navigate the twists and turns of casual sex. It's all about meeting new people, going on dates, and managing your sexual encounters. This is not just pickup strategy; these are techniques you can use to control your actions and take responsibility for your own pleasure.

When I was twenty, my typical response to a sexual proposition was, 'Sure, whatever.' Sometimes I didn't realise it was a bad decision until the whole thing was over. And if one of my partners got upset, I'd stand back and shrug my shoulders; not my problem. I didn't feel as though anything I said or did would make a difference.

I now know that I could have been having much more fun, if I'd only been a little more assertive.

As you know from Part I, casual sex is a high-octane ride, not a slow walk in the park. People can get hurt, physically and emotionally. When it comes to sex, nobody wants to look like a try-hard… and because the stakes are so high, it can seem scary to direct the action. If we just let things happen, it's easier to deny responsibility if something goes wrong. Except… making an effort is SO worth it.

When I started escorting, I was surprised to learn that everyone I met felt nervous in the bedroom. By speaking up, I was doing my partners a favour. Whether it was asking someone if they were comfortable, or negotiating a kinky activity, my partners were often grateful I was starting the conversation, because they were too scared to do it themselves.

Once the shy girl who was afraid to go to parties, I became the kind of person who could hook up with new friends with ease. It was an upward spiral: the more confident I felt, the better the sex… and the better the sex, the greater my confidence.

It feels hard—sometimes impossible—to go after what you want. But once you learn how, you'll have a power that few possess. All it takes is some essential skills, and a certain amount of practice. On the other hand, if you don't know this stuff, you might not be in control of your own journey.

I'd rather keep my hands on the wheel.

CHAPTER 4

HOW TO FIND YOUR PEOPLE

Times have changed.

When I was in high school, one of my friends met a woman from the USA on the Internet. They met in a chat room and hit it off. After a year of talking, she bought a plane ticket to Australia so that she could meet him. It didn't end in happily ever after, but she was thirty-five years old and my friend was eighteen, so perhaps we should have seen that coming. What I do remember was how much we made fun of him for meeting someone online. Aren't kids assholes?

Traditional dating used to be an in-person exercise. You met your partners through friends, at parties, or at work. Online dating sites were mostly used by divorcees and the socially awkward.

Nowadays, online dating is normalised. Almost everyone has used apps or websites to meet partners; we have instant access to thousands of people with whom we share nothing in common, apart from a mutual appreciation of our profile pics.

Getting to know someone without the benefit of body language is difficult. You have no information about them except whatever they've written in their bio or shared via their pictures. And, of course, they can unmatch or block you in a heartbeat. It's thrilling. It's also terrifying. It's the fast food of dating; you can match with someone, exchange words, and be dumped (or dump someone else) in a matter of minutes.

Online dating has advantages. It gives us a huge pool of potential partners, without needing to hang around at parties. Plus, there's less danger of invading someone's personal space, because you're both choosing to interact. Either person can cut off the conversation at will.

On the other hand, this strange new world isn't always a playground. There aren't any hard-and-fast rules. So, when I fire up my smartphone and start swiping, I meet people who want sex, who want relationships, who don't know how to start a conversation, or who just want to swap naked photos. It's difficult to work out who wants what, because we don't yet have an established social language to express our needs. I might spend the day chatting with a hot guy, to then learn he only wants to swap dirty pictures. I might take a few days getting to know a cute couple, then discover it's just the guy I've been talking with, because the girl doesn't want a threesome

Some of my friends struggle to go on dates at all. Even though there are hundreds of thousands of people online, getting a conversation started can be a challenge if you don't fit conventional standards of desirability. It's easy to feel as though online dating is letting you down, if the numbers aren't happening for you. The truth is, there's a knack to finding potential partners. Good matchmaking involves choosing the right people, keeping an open mind, and making genuine connections. Fortunately, all this stuff is totally learnable—that's what this chapter is for!

I'll be talking a lot about online dating apps because they're so commonly used, but the skills contained in this chapter are applicable to in-person experiences too.

Let's go find your people.

HOW TO FIND YOUR NICHE

We often feel as though trying to land a date is like dropping a fishing line in the ocean and hoping something bites. But the truth is, you have much more control over who is attracted to you than you might realise. The key to perfecting this is a business idea called 'niche marketing.'

Can you name the two objects pictured below? One is an everyday household item... the other holds the secret to attracting the right sexual partners.

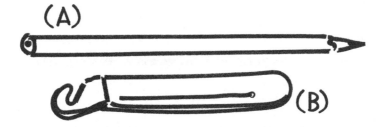

Exhibit A is a standard pencil. It's available in grocery stores and can be found on the desk of any office worker. It's cheap, easy to use, and universally recognised.

Exhibit B might be less familiar... unless you're a cycling enthusiast. It's a bicycle tyre lever—a tool used for changing a flat tyre quickly. If you ride over a nail on your morning commute, this little sucker will make your life much easier.

A bike tyre lever matters... to the right person. If I were to stand on a crowded street corner, hold a pencil up in the air and shout, 'Who wants to buy this?' I doubt I'd receive much attention. Almost everyone already has one and, like I said, they're not that exciting. But if I held the bike tool up and shouted about it for long enough, there's a decent chance that someone would purchase it. Maybe because they're a bike messenger and it's missing from their kit. Maybe because they just got a nail stuck in their wheel. Whatever. I can guarantee you that if someone did approach me, they'd be much more excited than if they were buying a pencil—because when someone needs a bike tyre lever, they REALLY need it.

This is what niche marketing is all about. The technical definition is, 'producing and selling a product to a specific segment of the market.' In the above example, the market is everyone in the street, and the segment is ONLY those people who might need to fix a puncture on their bike.

> **NICHE MARKETING:** Using your unique strengths to attract the people who are right for you.

What does this mean for online dating? For niche marketing on dating sites, the product is you. You need to work out what makes you different and advertise yourself to the segment of the dating population who want what you can offer. Whether you're an entertaining dinner guest, an expert camper, or a good hugger, your potential partners need to hear about it.

This might not sound appealing —you may worry that getting specific means you'll miss out. You might think making yourself look like a good catch for everyone will give you more options. But that's not how it works.

In dating, trying to please everyone means sticking to what we think of as conventional—average attractiveness, basic hobbies, no strong opinions. Remember how I said normal is bullshit? Trying to look average is weird… and worse, it's boring. It results in 'character beige'—a dating profile so inoffensive that even other regular folk will pass you by, in search of something more interesting.

There's a saying in marketing, 'if you try to appeal to everyone, you'll appeal to no one.' Trying to make everyone like you means looking so generic it makes you unrecognisable to the people you REALLY want – the ones who will find you irresistible.

Successful niche marketing requires a clear signal to your people. If you're a sci-fi nerd, tell the world. If you're obsessed with football, ditto. If you love having long conversations about the universe, I guarantee you that someone out there will appreciate that. Sure, it will decrease the number of potential matches, but the people who match with you are more likely to appreciate you. Plus, it'll help you skip the small talk and start connecting on a mutual interest straight away.

It's a short-term loss for long-term gain. I'd rather spend three hours swiping to get one good match than sit for three hours in a bar with a bad match, being forced to talk about football instead of philosophy!

I filter for guys who find strong women sexy. In my bio, I write 'I'm assertive and opinionated. If you're looking for a shy girl, that ain't me.' It may scare off the blokes who prefer quiet ladies, or don't enjoy women taking charge in the bedroom. But those men who appreciate outspoken women like me a lot.

QUESTIONS TO CONSIDER
- What are you passionate about?
- What are you good at?
- What makes you stand out from the crowd?
- What can you offer your partners?

Talk about what you're good at, and what you have to offer. Find the stuff that makes you unusual, and get a photo of it (or, even better, of you in it, on it, or doing it.) Don't consign yourself to Beige Land. Let your freak flag fly (or at least flap slightly in the wind.)

MAXIMISE YOUR MATCHES BY ADJUSTING YOUR EXPECTATIONS...

Your chosen market will affect your chances of finding a good match. When we get hung up on superficial qualities—age, body type, profession, etcetera—we limit our possibilities.

One of my escort clients has a middle-aged brother who went through a messy divorce. To cheer himself up, he began to frequent nightclubs, attempting to pick up twenty-year-olds. This did not work well, and he became even more dejected. But he should have thought it through a little better—his chosen market determined his (lack of) success.

There's nothing wrong with chatting up hotties, gym junkies or catwalk models. But you'd better have something great to offer if you're not hot, young, or ripped yourself. If you're a sixty-year-old retiree, you'll have better luck with other retirees than with lingerie models (unless you're paying them, of course). If you're a super-nerd who doesn't go outside much, you're going to do better with gamers than with adventure sports enthusiasts. Aiming to connect with people with similar interests or part of similar subcultures won't just improve your success rate; it'll also improve the quality of your interactions.

We all have an idea of the kind of hook-up partner we find desirable. Often, we inherit our tastes from our culture—there's a fixed idea of what's considered attractive. Sometimes it relates to the sort of porn we watch, or the people we see in the movies. There's nothing wrong with fantasy—it helps us work out what we're into. But if your tastes are inflexible (or unrealistic) then you risk missing other opportunities.

It's a hook up, not a marriage, so why not try something different? Widen the age range on your search options. Consider swiping right on brunettes as well as blondes. Chat to someone even if you're not sure whether they fit your preferences.

My work has an escort taught me to adjust my expectations. My clients come in all shapes and sizes, so I've had the chance to experiment with people who are different to those I normally date. I've discovered that being open-minded yields some rewarding hook ups. When I started working, I was into hot, gym-junkie twenty-five-year-olds. But after a few years of having sex with more diverse folks, I can confidently say that people from all walks of life make excellent hook-up partners. I've added several items to my list of attractive qualities: sharp wit, nice suits, redheads, bearded hipsters, shaved heads, skinny guys, long hair... every time I meet someone new, it's an opportunity to discover new things I like.

... BUT ALSO ENSURE YOUR REAL NEEDS ARE BEING MET

So, you've highlighted what makes you special, and gotten realistic about the people you want to attract. There's one more thing to do: work out what kind of people can actually give you what you need.

Remember the deeper needs we talked about in Chapter One? True satisfaction comes from connecting with partners who tick those specific boxes. Whether you're hoping for a romantic one-night stand, a kind escapade, or an intellectual connection, identifying the folks who are most likely to deliver will vastly increase your chances of a successful hook up.

Some of you might worry that having these criteria will make it harder to get dates. I know that many guys message hundreds of women just to get a few conversations happening. I understand that making that process more difficult might seem horrifying. But it doesn't work like that—having criteria gets you more dates, not fewer. Wanting to chat up absolutely anyone isn't a good look—it gives off the reek of desperation.

Imagine that you walk into a bar and sit down (I know, nobody goes to bars by themselves anymore, but I'm old, so humour me.) After a moment, an incredibly attractive person comes up to you. They say, 'Hi, I was wondering if you'd like to chat?' Of course, you say yes, they sit down, and you both start talking. Just as you'd expect from your perfect match, the conversation flows naturally and you're feeling comfortable around them.

You wonder, 'Is this too good to be true?' And because you're having such an honest conversation you ask, 'Why did you decide to talk to me?'

They might reply, 'Look, I've been sitting in this bar all night, and I was hoping I'd meet someone that I could have a really fun conversation with. But everyone who walked in looked depressed and grumpy. Then I saw you and you seemed so happy and sociable, you looked exactly like the kind of person I get along with. I figured it was worth a try.'

You'd be feeling pretty good about yourself at this point, right? But what if their answer was different?

Now imagine if they say, 'To be honest, I've been here all afternoon trying to pick up. I don't really care who it is, I've just been chatting to everyone and hoping someone will go on a date with me.'

Still feeling good? I'd guess not. Nobody enjoys being told that they're interchangeable with anyone else.

This is why we have criteria—not only does it prevent us looking desperate, it makes the right people feel valued. Pickup artists often fail simply because their aim is to get as many phone numbers (or as much sex) as possible. When you don't care who you hit on—when anyone would do—the people you approach don't feel special.

You can't fake having criteria. Negging doesn't work, not does pretending—people can smell bullshit a mile off. These need to be genuine standards, needs, and boundaries.

It's also useful to quiz yourself about the specific types of people that will rock your world.

USEFUL QUESTIONS

- **What do you REALLY want out of this?** As I said in Chapter One, it's not just about sex. What sort of person is most likely to provide the experience you're hoping for?

- **What flavour of sex are you looking for?** A regular missionary-position shag? Kinky stuff? Single-person or multiple people? Romantic, slow sex... or adventurous, wild wrestling?

- **What are your safety requirements?** What sort of people are you comfortable inviting home? How do they prove themselves trustworthy to you? (There's more about safety in the next chapter.)

- **What are your deal breakers?** What kind of behaviour or attributes are a hard 'no' for you? If you're a vegan who only dates vegans, or you can only fuck someone who can hold a conversation about astrophysics, keep that in mind when you put yourself out there.

- **What do you find sexy?** It's about personality, abilities, and interests… not just looks.

When putting this information in my dating profile, I find it useful to reframe the negatives as positives. Talking about the good qualities you're looking for will make a much better impression than complaining about stuff you don't like. Here are a few examples.

NEGATIVE	POSITIVE
"Shallow people suck!"	"I like folks who appreciate personality as well as looks."
"Lack of confidence is really unattractive."	"I'm looking for someone who isn't afraid to speak their mind."
"I'm tired of meeting assholes…"	"I love a guy who knows how to treat a woman right."
"I don't want any drama."	"Emotional maturity is welcome and appreciated!"
"Not here for a relationship."	"I'm looking for casual, sexy hangs with like-minded singles."

Having criteria is an attractive quality, especially if you focus on more than just appearance. Some of us are prouder of our brains than our bodies! If you define what you like about your match as a person, it'll make a great impression.

Note I said 'criteria', not standards. It's not about judging people and deciding whether they're worthy of your attention. It's about working out whether your potential date is someone you'd enjoy spending more time with. We're not designed to get along with everyone in the world; we need those who can genuinely give us what we need.

When you have criteria, it shows that you know what you want. Those matches who are right for you will feel valued. Even if you still need make lots of approaches to get one conversation, setting some requirements will improve your attractiveness.

YOUR CRASH COURSE IN DIVERSITY

Are you a guy that's into shagging guys? Do you prefer cuddling to fucking? Do you feel more like a lady, when your parents thought you were a bloke? Maybe some of this applies to you, or maybe it doesn't. But even if you don't relate, I can guarantee you've met people that do. To be a good catch, you need to be comfortable around people who are different to you.

GENDER AND SEXUAL DIVERSITY:
All the ways we differ from each other around who we fuck, who we date, what gender we are, and what our bits look like.

The Australian Human Rights Commission estimates that eleven percent of Aussies are gender or sexually diverse. This means that more than one in ten of us fuck or date in ways that differ from the majority… or have genders that differ from what we were assumed to be at birth.

The world's changing. I'm not saying gender and sexually diverse people didn't exist before now, but they used to have to hide away a lot more than they do today. This is the curse of 'normal'—when folk are don't fit in, they get judged. Luckily, we're starting to get used to the idea that everyone's different. It's good for sexually and gender diverse people… and it's good for you too, no matter your orientation.

SOME WORDS YOU NEED TO KNOW

- **Gender identity** means how male, female, or 'other' you are. Everyone has a slightly different balance, and it's more about how you feel than what you look like.

- **Gender expression** is how you dress, act, and appear to the rest of the world.

- **Biological sex** refers to what your genitals look like (whether you have a cock, a pussy, ovaries, testes, something in-between, or even both—that happens too).

- **Physical attraction** is who you fuck or play with (what's usually referred to as 'sexual orientation', although it's not just about sex).

- **Emotional attraction** is who you're romantically interested in.

The people you meet don't always announce their differences straight away— it may take time to discover them. For example, to the casual observer I look like a straight, thirty-something woman—but I'm actually a bisexual, non-binary-gendered kinkster. Surprise! (As far as I'm concerned, surprises are half the fun of getting to know new people.)

When I say I'm bisexual, I'm referring to my sexual attraction to people of all genders. When I say I'm non-binary, I'm talking about my gender identity—I don't feel much like a woman on the inside. But when it comes to gender expression, I look pretty darn female. And that's okay.

Being comfortable around diversity is a top-notch hook-up skill, for a number of reasons:

- **It gives you more options.** Accepting diverse people means you'll have more potential partners.
- **You won't freak out** if you meet someone different to yourself; this saves embarrassment and awkwardness.
- **Being safe and respectful is sexy;** it's an excellent dating strategy.
- **It helps you get your head around the fact that everyone is different,** and maybe even allows you to cut yourself some slack, if your desires or appearance don't feel normal.

Sex and gender diverse people use various words to refer to themselves. Here are a few of the basic ones.

COMMON TERMS FOR DIVERSE FOLK

- **LGBTQIA+**—this is called an 'umbrella term' because it refers to lots of diverse people (gay, lesbian, bisexual, transgender, queer, intersex, asexual, etc.) If you meet someone that says they're LGBTQIA+ it means you can't make any assumptions about who they fuck, how they do it, or what bits they do it with. If you get sexy with them, it's your job to ask.

- **Queer**—as above, this can refer to diversity in sexuality, gender identity, or romantic preferences. Don't assume you know what your queer date is into! You need to ask.

- **Transgender/Cisgender**—these terms are all about your gender: how masculine/feminine/other you feel on the inside (not what you have in your pants). If you feel like a different gender to the one you were assigned at birth, that's called being transgender. If your feelings match the label you were given when you were born, that's called being cisgender.

- **Gay/lesbian**—peeps who are attracted to the same gender as themselves.

- **Bisexual/pansexual**—folk who are attracted to a variety of genders, or all genders.

- **Heteroflexible/homoflexible**—someone who occasionally strays from their preferred gender to hook up with other types of people. For example, I have a few male friends who are into women but might sometimes have sex with guys on Grindr—if you like variety, it's great to keep your options open! It's worth noting that some people simply never feel the urge to experiment; that's fine too. You don't need to be heteroflexible or homoflexible just for the street cred. Do what makes you happy.

Honestly, it's usually impossible to tell who is straight and who is gay or who is trans and who isn't, just by looking at someone (or even by checking out their junk, if you're getting sexy with them). Some gay folks are obviously so, some are not. Transfolk can have various types of genitalia, and different names for their bits, too. It's easy to get stressed out about this—lots of people don't like not knowing for sure, not being able to stick a label on someone. The way I see it, who cares? If you're attracted to someone who's attracted to you, it's just a matter of asking them what they need, using the sexy comunication skills we're going to talk about in Part II. In addition, here are a few ideas that can help.

TIPS FOR TREATING DIVERSE FOLK RIGHT

- **Respect their identity and pronouns.** If you met someone called Ted, but you insisted on calling him Bruce every time you saw him, he'd get pissed off, right? People have a right to be addressed the way they want. If you refuse to use your hook up's preferred name and pronouns (he and him, her and she, they and them, etc.) you're going to look like a dick.

- **Treat your dates like people, not sex objects.** Sometimes people obsess over hooking up with a particular type of person. We call this fetishising—focusing on one characteristic and forgetting to see the whole person. It often happens to transwomen, lesbians, bisexual women, people of colour and ethnic minorities (e.g., 'Asian women are hot!') You may think telling someone they're attractive is a compliment, but if you're only interested in their race, gender, or sexuality, it makes them feel like zoo exhibits.

- **Don't ask what someone has in their pants.** Being gender diverse is not necessarily about having a dick when you're a lady, or vice versa. Asking them about it is like walking up to a dude in a bar and saying, 'how big is your cock exactly?' There are certain things you don't get to find out until you become intimate with someone.

- **Ask before touching.** Our bodies all work differently. Not every transperson can get an erection. Not everyone who identifies as female enjoys penetrative sex. Some people don't like being touched in certain areas or in certain ways, and it's awful when a sexual partner just grabs without asking first. If you're getting sexy with someone, ask, 'how do you like to be touched?' or, 'What sort of sex are you into?' Asking is much less awkward than fucking it up.

You might be thinking, 'I'm never going on a date with a gay guy, so why does this stuff matter? Apart from the fact that being okay with queer folk makes you look like an ace human being, there's also another advantage: learning to be okay with your own differences. Even if the thing that makes you weird is your pet turtle, or the mole on your forehead, accepting others helps us to remember to be kind to ourselves too.

HOW TO WRITE YOUR DATING PROFILE

Find it difficult to write about yourself? You're not alone. Unfortunately, this hurdle must be overcome. Fortunately, it's not complicated..

The purpose of the text on your online dating profile is to provide enough information to allow people to decide whether they're interested in what you have to offer. A profile picture isn't enough to know someone.

You're looking for connection, and connection relies on more than the physical. Your prospective partner doesn't just need to see your face. They need more information—about you, your interests, your personality, and what you're looking for. It's not enough to find your niche… you must express it to others, so that they recognise you as someone they'd get along with. I see a lot of hot people online, but I won't send a message unless I can read about them first.

Similarly, you might not get matches if you don't have decent profile photos. I'm not talking about professional shots… but there's a certain minimum standard required.

Creating a decent profile doesn't have to be complicated. Here are the basics.

FOUR STEPS WRITING YOUR DATING PROFILE

1. **Say something about yourself.** This is where your niche marketing comes into play. Tell the world what you're about, what you're into, and what you have to offer. And remember, beige is boring! 'I'm a backyard handstand addict who dreams of running away with the circus,' is better than 'My name is Tom and I'm an accountant.'

2. **Be honest about what you're looking for.** This is where you set some standards. Keep it positive, e.g., 'I'm looking for a fun, mutually beneficial arrangement,' or 'Let's spend the night in bed talking about the mysteries of the universe.'

3. **Signal to your social group.** Don't be afraid to mention your fave Netflix series, dank meme, or 17th-Century novelist. An obscure reference is A-okay, if your niche understands and appreciates the reference.

4. **Encourage conversation.** Drop a question, joke, or conversation starter. I have a friend who writes, 'Fuck, marry, or kill: Batman, Superman, Wolverine?' It gives her matches something to talk about, and it also weeds out those who don't have a sense of humour.

MY DATING PROFILE

Writer, entrepreneur, sex nerd. I'm assertive and opinionated. If you're looking for a shy gal, that ain't me! Let's get through a bottle of shiraz together and swap ideas for world domination.

Not looking for a long-term relationship - just a hook-up with someone fun who knows how to hold a great conversation.

GGG. Tell me about your last big adventure, not your Myers-Briggs classification. 😂

FOUR ESSENTIAL DATING PROFILE PHOTOS

1. **Face**—you need a clear shot of your face. No duck face, no filters, no weird angles. This is not necessarily conventional physical attractiveness—often it's about your smile or your eyes. We learn a lot about someone's personality by looking at their expression!

2. **Body**—include a clear body photo. It sucks, but people have preferences. They might not always be what you think- I have lady friends who love dad bods and guy friends who love curvy chicks. The important thing is to weed out anyone who isn't into your body type, so you don't waste your time on them.

3. **Interests**—This is where you shine, from a niche marketing point of view! Your interests, hobbies, something that shows your character—

go for it. This is where the travel photos go. Or if you have a rock collection, fine. Use it.

4. **Social**—This is the photo of you with friends, so we know you have social skills. The social setting will say a lot about the kind of person you are. For example, I'll never pick a guy who posts a photo of himself having fun at a wedding, because I absolutely hate weddings. If you're a loner and you're looking for quiet people, here's where you post a photo of yourself reading a book.

Progress is better than perfection—I'd rather get my dating profile up and tweak it later than spend hours agonising over every word. Set up your profile, see who matches, repeat. As you experiment, you'll move closer to attracting the right people.

TL;DR

- Use niche marketing to find the people that really like you.
- Keep it realistic—forget supermodels, regular people are sexy too…
- But knowing your standards is incredibly attractive.
- Being comfortable around diverse folk makes you look like a good human being and reminds you to accept your own differences.
- Writing a dating profile can feel like challenge, but it's not as hard as it seems. Say something about yourself, be honest about what you're looking for, signal to your social group, and use a conversation starter.
- Include a range of photos—show your face, body, hobbies, and social life.

Once you've encountered a potential match, what next? Well, I want you to charm the pants off them (literally). But before you do, there some things you need to know. Next up is Essential Strategy: hook-up philosophies that will guide you towards a better sexual experience.

CHAPTER 5

ESSENTIAL STRATEGY

Being a sexpert isn't just about the way you think—it's also about the way you act. When skills, attitude and actions align, that's the recipe for an amazing hook up.

If you don't believe me, just ask Hugo.

Hugo is a friend of mine. He's twenty-eight and on a disability pension because his back is 'severely fucked up' (his words, not mine). Sometimes the pain is so bad that he can't sit down for more than a few minutes. He's quiet, wears glasses, and loves books. He seems like the kind of guy who doesn't often speak to women. But that's where you'd be wrong.

We meet for coffee on the regular. 'How was your week?' I ask him.

'It was good.' he says. 'I had a date with a new person on Wednesday, and I didn't expect it to get sexy, but it did! And then on Friday I had a threesome with one of my partners and her friend, something we'd been planning for a while. By the way, are you going to the sex party tonight? I have some fun stuff planned with an awesome couple I met last week.'

Hugo, you see, is a sex god. Sex is my job, but Hugo gets laid more than I do.

It can't be easy—he's often in too much pain to walk down the stairs of his apartment. Nevertheless, he manages to get out into the world, find his people, make friends with them and have plenty of sexy encounters.

We often assume that hot people get more sex. Dating success is associated with typical masculinity and femininity: buff, macho guys and skinny, blonde women. People who aren't conventionally attractive are considered losers.

Hugo is living proof that this is not how the world works.

This guy has the moves. I'm not just talking about sex skills (although he has those too.) I'm talking about his ability to see his dates as people first, and playmates second. When his lovers emerge from his bedroom, they tell everyone what a great guy he is, including other potential partners in his social circle. And so, it continues; Hugo hooks up with his friends, his hook ups talk about how great he is, he gets laid even more. He has a successful love life because he knows how to connect, and his skills that keep people coming back.

At this point, I imagine you're keen to get stuck into the sexy stuff. We've just talked about finding the right people, and how to engage in a conversation that encourages them say 'Want to grab a beer?' I promise we're almost there… but we have a little more head-examining to do first, to ensure you're on top of your game.

Connection, integrity, honesty, safety. This stuff can turn you into a hook-up champion! But it isn't something you can just slap on like a coat of paint.

Your dates will eventually catch on if it's not sincere. To get it right, you'll need to work on your attitude, not just your pickup lines.

This chapter tackles the following:

1. Why **connection is essential** for good sex.
2. Why **you shouldn't be an asshole** to the people you fuck.
3. **Radical honesty** (how and why it works).
4. **The importance of safety**, for all genders.

Changing our behaviour is difficult, especially when nobody else seems to be making the effort. But Hugo has been doing it for years, and it works for him. It might just work for you too.

CONNECTION IS THE #1 SEX MOVE

We spend most of our time in this life alone, bouncing around inside our own heads. Even when we're surrounded by friends and family, we can still feel lonely. Connection is that feeling you get when someone acknowledges your existence—through eye contact, listening to you speak, a hug, or a kind word.

Connection means being tuned in to your partner so that their feelings, thoughts, and needs become important to you. It isn't just for hippies and tantra fanatics - it's a basic technique that can increase your chances of hooking up and give you a better sexual experience.

Sex is biologically designed to help us feel connected. When we come into close physical contact with someone we're attracted to, our brains release chemicals that make us feel 'bonded' to the other person. It becomes easier to share our feelings, and we get a rush similar to being high. This is why we refer to love as a 'drug'.

These chemical reactions don't just happen with romance... they occur during hook ups, too.

How good we feel during a casual encounter depends on the quality of the connection we have with our date. A great connection makes hook ups better because we end up in 'sync'—all those little things like timing, eye contact, and body language happen at the right times, so that everything seems natural and effortless. It's almost like magic—when you're tuned in to your partner, time flows faster, and you lose awareness of the outside world.

Good connection means letting someone see you for who you are—and that's powerful. It makes you feel as though you're not alone in the universe.

When we hook up with people, but the connection isn't there, the physical stuff often feels mechanical. We tend to see people as objects that we can use to satisfy our own needs, so we treat them badly. And we feel lonely, even when we're actually getting laid. Sex without connection is usually bad sex.

I have a friend called Alicia who is a swinger, and she complains that most of the people she and her husband meet online don't want to take the time to connect before getting it on. 'They just want to skip straight to the play, they can't be bothered getting to know us,' she says. 'We want to fuck people that we've made friends with first.'

Alicia says, 'All sex starts in the brain.' If you don't take an interest in the person you want to fuck, why bother fucking them at all? You're missing out on 99% of the fun.

Knowing how to connect is a powerful skill that can make you a very attractive prospect. The secret lies in four basic qualities.

THE ESSENTIAL INGREDIENTS OF CONNECTION

- **Honesty**—Seeing the other person for who they are letting them see who you are.
- **Respect**—treating their body, their rights, and their opinions with as much concern as your own.
- **Trust**—showing you're safe to be around and allowing them to demonstrate their trustworthiness.
- **Attention**—being focused on what they're saying, doing and feeling in the moment, and having their attention in return.

Connection is a wonderful antidote to creepiness - that uncomfortable feeling of having your personal space invaded, or realising you've invaded someone else's.

When we're only interested in people for what they can give us, we tend to misss the signs that we're making them uneasy. When we take a genuine interest in them, we can find out what they actually want from us—a much more enjoyable situation, for everyone.

Sometimes I screw this up—when I'm horny, I look at every guy I see on the street through the lens of, 'Is he fuckable?' and I start to feel like a total perv. I remind myself that hot people don't owe me anything; they probably have other things on their minds. If you can stay curious about the person instead of focusing on getting laid, your job is half done.

The next chapter gives you some practical tips on connecting with your hook up, but you need to get your attitude right first. A genuine desire to connect is your most powerful move.

WHY YOU SHOULDN'T BE AN ASSHOLE

Being nice to people is good for you.

Have you ever come home from a date feeling like shit? I don't just mean the ones that leave you feeling underwhelmed. I mean the ones where you open your front door, drop your bag on the floor, throw yourself on the couch and wish you'd never gone out in the first place? The ones that require you to call your friends and have them take you out for wine and hug you until you feel lovable again? The ones that make you declare, 'That's it. I'd rather be celibate than have this stuff happen to me.' When other people treat us badly, it feels as though the universe itself is saying, 'You're not worthy.'

Although we all know what it's like to be treated badly, most of us have also been awful to someone else. Be honest—when was the last time you ignored someone's messages because you didn't know how to say, 'I'm not interested'? Have you ever fucked someone who had romantic feelings for you, even though you didn't want a relationship? Do you ever look down on a person you don't find attractive?

Most people call these behaviours 'dick moves', but I call them 'asshole moves' because it's not always guys that are the culprits.

COMMON ASSHOLE MOVES

- **Ghosting**—ignoring someone's messages and calls without explanation, because it's easier to leave them hanging than to say 'sorry, not interested.'

- **Breadcrumbing**—mostly ignoring, but still responding to a sexual partner's messages or calls every now and again, in case you decide you want to fuck them again in the future.

- **Standing people up**—this is when you don't turn up to a date and leave someone waiting for you (and questioning their life choices).

- **Letting someone believe you want a romantic relationship, so you can have sex with them.** If you have no intention of reciprocating their feelings but don't make that clear, it's a total asshole move.

- **Pressuring someone into sex**—badgering them until they give in, or waiting until they're drunk… at best it's harassment, at worst it's sexual assault.

- **Shaming someone** for their body / skin colour / kinks / dick size / disability / anything else.

- **Fucking someone and not checking whether they're enjoying themselves.** If you're just in it for your own pleasure, they can tell—and being used sucks.

- **Expecting your date to be a mind-reader, then blaming them when they get it wrong.** I know sometimes it's hard to be honest about what you want. But we're not psychic; getting angry at your partner when they don't provide exactly what you need is unfair, if you haven't taken the trouble to ask. This situation sucks when it's about choosing a movie on date night… and it REALLY sucks during flirting and sex. If you want someone to invite you on a date or engage in a particular sexual activity… you need to ask.

I dumped my first boyfriend when I was sixteen. I can't even remember the reason. We had 'the conversation' during gym class; he was jogging alongside me, trying to understand why I was ending the relationship. I shouted, 'I'm not sad about it, and you shouldn't be either!' Then I ran off and left him behind… it was heartless. Did he cry? I don't know—I was too busy sprinting away.

Sometimes we don't want to be nice. Sometimes communication is difficult. Sometimes we don't know what we want. Sometimes it's easier to throw our hands in the air than to deal with a difficult sexual situation. We make assholes out to be monsters but forget that we ourselves often behave badly when we don't know what to do. Honesty is difficult, and it leaves us vulnerable; sometimes we're tempted to skip all that and go straight for what we want, even though we know it's going to harm someone else.

Here's why you shouldn't be an asshole.

1. YOU RUIN IT FOR EVERYONE ELSE.

Why does this even matter? Why not burn your bridges? It's not like you're interested in that person anyway, does it matter if they never want to speak to you again? Plenty more fish in the sea, right?

Well, you might be okay with burning that bridge, but you're also burning it for someone else. The next person who tries to get close to the date you fucked with is going to have to deal with the hurt you caused. And while you're out there burning people's bridges, other folks are burning yours. You know that woman you approached, who looked scared? Someone put that fear there. You know the guy who didn't want to get naked with you because someone made fun of his dick once? Same deal.

The more we act like assholes, the more wounded and fucked-up people there will be. Wounded and fucked-up people are hard to hook up with, because they don't trust anyone.

We need to stop fucking things up for everyone, and it must start somewhere. Do the right thing and demand your partners do right by you. Call out your friends if you see them treating their dates badly. Let's make this game fun, instead of a total shit-show.

2. IT'S HARD TO FAKE 'GOOD.'

When you meet someone you like, you want them to think you're a good person. You want them to trust you, because that's how the sex bit happens. But it's no use telling them. People who say, 'I'm one of the good guys' are a dime a dozen; it doesn't mean they'll follow through.

I've found that folks can sense assholery—even if they can't put their finger on it, they will feel uneasy. You can't fake being a decent person. You can only demonstrate it via your actions. If you spend most of your time being an asshole, the smell of bullshit is going to waft off you every time you try to impress someone new.

Being nice: it's good for you, and good for getting you laid. Although using and abusing might seem like the easy option, in the long run everyone suffers.

BREAKING THE RULES WITH RADICAL HONESTY

We spend most of our lives avoiding telling the truth. I'm not saying this as a criticism, just a statement of fact. Most of our conversations involve hiding our intentions: because it's polite, because we don't want to be weird, because we're afraid someone will say 'no'. Sometimes even a simple 'how are you?' doesn't get an honest answer. From complimenting your Aunt on her bad cooking to hiding the fact that you're gay at work, lying is often a matter of social convenience. As a result, everything that comes out of our mouths has a hidden meaning. You greet your neighbour with a 'good morning', but you both know you're flirting. Or you say, 'Hey, dickhead' to your best friend, and mean it as a sign of affection.

All this vagueness makes it hard to work out what's going on during a sexual encounter.

I went on a date with a guy who seemed awesome at first… but turned out to be a bit of an asshole. I'm not going to name him, because he probably wouldn't appreciate being mentioned in this book. Basically, we matched online, met up, and had a few drinks. I thought he was cute, and I made it clear that I was interested. But neither of us said the magic words, 'what are you looking for?' This was our mistake.

I took him home, and we got some crazy bedroom gymnastics happening. After we'd finished, he said, 'I have to let you know that I'm busy and I don't have time to date you.' The words left his mouth literally thirty seconds after he came; I didn't even have time to put my pants back on.

I was pissed off, not because I had my heart set on dating him, but because he'd been dishonest. He'd known before we had sex that he wasn't available in the long term—it had probably been on his mind the whole time we were banging. But he'd waited until afterwards to tell me, because he wanted to make sure he got laid first. The most annoying thing was, if he'd told me beforehand, I would have fucked him anyway. It was the fact that he decided to lie to me that I found awful. I felt used, when I should have felt appreciated.

Lying before (and during, and after) sex creates confusion. The solution is to get the hang of being honest—about your feelings, your intentions, and who you are as a person. When you speak up, your partner won't have to guess what's going on inside your head. In dating, radical honesty cuts through the crap and lets you get straight to the action.

Telling the truth often feels like breaking the rules—there's this unspoken idea that we're not supposed to talk about our feelings or our bodies. But when you do, you take a shortcut past the sex-negativity and insecurity that often come along for the ride when we go on a date. It feels like cheating—I guess, by the rules of modern society, it is! But if you can confidently state what you want and how you feel, you're going to stand out. It's a quick way to elevate yourself above the competition.

When I'm honest, I get some interesting reactions. If I feel the date isn't going great, or if I'm not attracted to the person, I say so. I'm not an ass-hole—I don't give my date a hard time. Rather, I say, 'Hey, I wanted to let you know that I'm not feeling a sexual connection. Still happy to have a drink and chat, though!'

Sometimes folks freak out when I say this. Sometimes they feel bad, because they haven't yet learned to handle a gentle rejection. But almost all of them thank me for being straight with them. I get the impression that, in the past, they have experienced the frustration of not knowing that a potential partner wasn't interested. They tell me it's refreshing to not have to puzzle it out in silence.

USEFUL LINES

- **On an uninspiring date:** 'You're great, but I'm not feeling a con-nection.'
- **When you're trying to avoid a romantic relationship**: 'Just to let you know, I'm not looking for anything serious.'
- **When you find your date attractive:** 'I think you're really cute—just putting that out there!'
- **When you think they might be DTF:** 'I'm getting a vibe that maybe I should invite you back to my place? Am I right?'
- **When the sex could be better:** 'A bit more to the left, thanks! Perfect.'
- **When you don't want to do something:** 'Sorry, I'm not into that.'
- **When you don't want someone staying over:** 'Hope this is okay, but I don't let dates sleep over.'

- **When they have something in their teeth:** 'Um, you've got something in your teeth.'

Similarly to assholedom, dishonesty in dating happens because we don't have the words or the confidence. Our culture doesn't encourage talking about our feelings. As a result, lots of folks haven't had enough practice at communication and they have no idea what to say... or don't understand why it's important in the first place.

Also, being honest is scary. Letting your feelings out leaves you vulnerable to rejection. It's hard to say, 'I like you' if you're afraid someone will laugh at you, or 'Hey, want to hook up?' if you worry about being told to get lost. Even something as simple as saying 'No, I don't want to do that,' can be terrifying, because if our 'no' is ignored then we know for sure that the other person doesn't care about us. Often it seems easier just to shut up and pretend we're okay.

The problem is, failing to communicate means we're unlikely to be satisfied. Our partners aren't mind-readers. No matter how experienced or confident your date seems, they still don't know you as well as you know yourself; mastering honesty is the most effective way to get what you need.

You might be thinking 'If I'm honest about wanting to hook up, I'll never get laid.' If you feel this way—if you're sure there's no way anyone would fuck you unless you trick them into it—your attitude is your biggest obstacle. I have friends of all ages and levels of physical attractiveness who enjoy casual sex. They succeed by being honest, respectful, and taking a genuine interest in their lovers.

My barista Thomas is happily married, but when he was single, he hooked up with plenty of women. One afternoon while I was writing in his café, he sat opposite me and gave me a piece of his mind.

He said, 'When I was picking up at bars, I'd be totally up front. If I'd slept with another woman the night before, I said so. If I wasn't interested in dating, I made sure they knew it. You'd think that saying that stuff would ruin my chances, but it had the opposite effect. The ladies I hit on were stoked that I was being straight with them. Also,' he added with a grin, 'they told all their friends.'

By now, you've probably noticed that I'm not a fan of pickup artists. I reckon any time someone offers to show you a shortcut to getting laid, they're full of shit. But I will say that being honest is a game-changer, when it comes to making new sexy friends. Telling the truth is unexpected—it allows us to side-step social convention a little and opens more possibilities for conversation (and action).

The key to making honesty work for you is a good delivery. Confidence and keeping things casual are both essential.

I had a gym coach whose delivery was perfect. He could get away with anything, from severe criticism of our lifting technique to the most disgusting jokes. I once observed him saying to a client, 'Bro, I love you, but if you leave your weights out on the floor again, I'm going to kick your ass out of here.' Then he walked away, as though he'd had the most natural conversation in the world. The dude he'd lectured didn't even look pissed off; it was as if they'd shared a bonding experience.

A combination of casual delivery, confidence, and compassion is the key. Everybody who witnessed that incident knew that my coach was dead serious—he would have banned the guy from the gym if necessary. But because his honesty was delivered well, it ended in a smile rather than an argument. And it worked: the dude stopped leaving his weights out.

HOW TO BE HONEST WITHOUT BEING AN ASSHOLE

- **Make it about you**—stick to 'I' statements, e.g. 'I don't feel comfortable meeting at your place.' That way you're not shaming the other person, just sharing your feelings.

- **Be caring**—we're trying to be compassionately honest, not brutally honest. If your date isn't your type, it's better to say, 'Sorry, I'm not feeling a connection,' than 'Sorry, I don't find you attractive in the slightest.' Being compassionately honest is good for the receiver as well as the giver—if you're not interested in dating someone it's kinder to let them know quickly, so that they can move on to someone else.

- **Be confident**—you might not feel confident the first few times you try this stuff. But I've found that the more confident I feel, the more likely my partner is to accept me, no matter how much crazy honesty I'm throwing at them. If you can pull it off, act as if being honest is something you do all the time. But even if you're totes awkward, practise will make it easier.

- **Notice your power**—sometimes when we assume we're just making an innocent comment, the other person feels pressured. One example of this: your boss says, 'I think you're cute.' It's honest, but since she's your boss you might worry about losing your job if you don't respond positively to her flirtation. If someone is in a vulnerable position, you need to consider whether being honest is okay, or whether to take a step back.

Occasionally, I'm judged for speaking up. This is why we did all that emotional bullet-proofing work in Part I. But I've found that the more honest I am, the less I worry about what other people think. There's a strength you can grow in yourself by choosing to be open to others. Psychologist Brené Brown says it best in her book *Daring Greatly*:

Vulnerability sounds like truth and feels like courage. Truth and courage aren't always comfortable, but they're never weaknesses.

When I put all my weird, scared stuff out on display, it's harder for people to attack me for who I am. When I own my needs and opinions, people tend to respect that, even if they don't agree.

When you're honest, people assume you're strong—and you are.

SAFETY IS FOR EVERYONE

Safety—what is it, exactly?

If you've ever had your wallet stolen or been punched in the schoolyard, you have an idea of what being in danger looks like. This is what's called physical safety—making sure that nobody injures you, deprives you of your possessions, or hinders your freedom.

If you're a guy and you think physical safety on dates is a women's problem, think again. I once knew a guy whose date brought a gun in her handbag when she met him! Another of my friends was trapped in his house by a person suffering from mental illness wielding a kitchen knife. Although women are at greater risk of physical violence, bad stuff happens to everyone.

Less obvious are the psychological dangers. Being picked on, put down, lied to… it sucks. And it's not just sticks and stones, either. We like to think words don't hurt, but sometimes they do.

When you hook up with someone, you're in a vulnerable situation. Good means getting close to your partner, both physically and mentally. If you're holding back, you're not going to have a good experience. But there's huge potential for them to damage you, through words or actions. If a guy takes a swing at you in the street, you might be able to get away… but if they try it when you're alone, you're at much greater risk of physical harm. If you've just spent two hours drinking with a stranger and they tell you you're unattractive, you might feel bad… but if you have sex with them and they say it afterwards, it's going to feel much, much worse. We all know this—it's why going on dates feels so nerve-wracking.

Over the course of my career in sex work, I've become experienced at sensing fear—both in myself and others. If I don't feel safe, I'm on edge the whole time. On the other hand, once I feel secure, I can stop watching my back and start enjoying myself.

It's not just about you; your date is probably nervous too. The more you can help your partner feel secure, the closer they will allow themselves to get to you.

Here are some practical ideas.

TRUST YOUR GUT

This is the most important piece of safety advice I can give you. My self-defence coach used to put it this way: 'All the training in the world won't help you if you don't see that first punch coming.' The best defence isn't offence; it's getting out before the trouble starts (or avoiding it in the first place.)

I once went out drinking with a couple of blokes. One was my then-boyfriend, and the other was a new friend of his. The friend was a seriously big guy who worked out a lot. As the night progressed, my BF's friend became more and more drunk. He started saying offensive sexual stuff to women on the street. Then he made sexual comments about me, which was really uncomfortable.

At the end of the night, this asshole followed us home. He tried to follow me right through the front door of my house. My boyfriend was almost passed-out drunk, and totally useless. I looked at the other guy, standing at the door, and I knew that if I let him in, I was going to be sexually assaulted. He hadn't said so to my face—I just had this sense of foreboding. It felt physical, a sick feeling in my stomach.

I did something brave; the bravest thing I had ever done in my life. I told him to go home and slammed the door shut in his face. It was rude; he was offended. But I'd rather have someone be angry at me than end up being attacked.

I was lucky. Not everyone gets a gut feeling before something bad happens. But if you do get that feeling, don't ignore it.

ARRANGE A SAFE CALL

A safe call is a procedure whereby you tell a trusted friend your location and instruct them to get help if they don't hear from you within a certain time. In the escorting biz we use these all the time, because we're often going to homes or hotels to meet people we don't know. Us escorts are safety pros.

HOW TO SET UP A SAFE CALL

1. **Ask a reliable friend.** Give them the details, including the name and phone number of the person you're meeting. If you get into a car, message your friend with the registration number. If you go home with your date, message your friend the address. Agree on a time to 'check in' by phone—this could be halfway through the night, or it could be when you leave for home, or it could be the next morning. Agree on what will happen if you don't check in—will your friend call the police? Will they come looking for you?

2. **Make sure your date knows about the safe call.** 'Hey, I have to call a friend at ten o'clock. She knows I'm on this date and she wants to hear how it's going.' This is the most important step for keeping you safe. You want your date to know that you have a safety plan.

3. **If you feel unsafe, call your friend immediately.** You don't need to scream 'Help!' into the phone, if that would be too obvious. It's enough to let your friend say, 'Is everything ok?' and reply 'Nah.' At that point, your mate should launch into emergency mode and do all the things you've planned.

4. **If the date goes well, check in at the correct time.** Don't forget to make the call! A few cop cars turning up to your date's house is not a great way to end the night.

MEET IN A PUBLIC PLACE

Never invite a stranger directly into your home.

In the previous story, I was able to fend off disaster by making sure that a dodgy guy didn't get into my house. Saying 'fuck off' was terrifying. He was massive; he looked as though he'd be able to break it down. I can't imagine how I would have gotten him to leave if he'd stepped through the door.

Avoiding danger means giving your intuition as much time as possible to make an assessment. Meeting for a drink or a coffee is an absolute must: engage your partner in conversation long enough that they let their guard down. (This also allows time to cultivate that awesome connection we talked about earlier.)

Outdoor first-date activities can be fun... but consider your safety, even when you're in public. A trip to the arcade parlour is awesome, but a long walk through a park at night could be just as dangerous as bringing someone home.

LOOK OUT FOR RED FLAGS

When I match with a guy on Tinder who asks me out for a drink after the first few messages, I always reply, 'Dude, no. You haven't passed the Psycho Test yet.'

The Psycho Test is something we do in our heads without even thinking about it. As we're talking to a new person, we process the verbal and non-verbal clues they give us, to work out if they're safe. There are so many things that signal whether someone is legit, and there are plenty of signs that show someone isn't. The warning signs are called 'red flags.'

> **RED FLAG:** A warning sign that could mean trouble further down the road.

MY RED FLAGS

- **Pushiness**—if my potential date pushes me for personal sexual information or insists on getting my number before we meet, I assume they will be pushy in person too.

- **Weird shit**—okay, I'm a little weird myself! But sometimes the conversation gets too wacky, or stops making sense, which might mean they aren't on my wavelength (or perhaps just drunk or stoned).

- **Being sleazy**—if someone is talking dirty as soon as we match, without any discussion as to what we're both looking for, it's a hint that they might be sexually inappropriate in person.

- **Sounding angry/negative**—this stuff should be fun, right? Why hang out with someone who's wearing their grumpy pants?

- **Trying to meet up straight away**—when someone wants to meet before we have even worked out whether we get along, it's suspicious. It indicates bad judgement. Why would you meet someone even though you know nothing about them, and risk wasting everyone's time?

Everyone has different standards. It takes me a couple hours of chatting, or a few dozen messages, to get an idea. Follow your own process... but don't try to rush it, no matter how badly you want to!

TEST YOUR PARTNER

As I'm getting to know someone, I test them to see how they react to my boundaries. Asking simple things, such as, 'Can we sit at another table instead?' helps indicate whether my date is a decent person. If they give me a hard time, then I know they might not respect my other, more important, preferences.

As the date is progressing, I sometimes say, 'I'm not sure if I want to hook up tonight, can we talk for a while and I'll let you know later on?' If you try this and your partner doesn't take it seriously, it could be a sign that they don't like hearing 'no'.

Conversation often gives us lots of useful red flags, like I described in the previous section. 'Do you get along with your exes?' is a great question to get a feel for how they treat other people. Even their way of speaking can offer clues—are they relaxed or irritable? Positive or grumpy? Everything someone does and says can help indicate what they're like as a person.

HELP OTHERS FEEL SAFE

Part of the job of being a good lover is the care and consideration you show others. I don't mean you need to go all counsellor on their asses or treat them like children; supporting their safety concerns is easy. If they say, 'I have to be home by midnight,' respect that. If they say, 'I prefer to meet for a coffee first,' enthusiastically agree. Your actions speak louder than your words.

I had an amazing make-out session with a hot guy once, on the couch in his apartment. Halfway through he said, 'I have a rule that I won't fuck anyone on the first date, but I feel like I want to break it right now!'

My response was, 'Let's stick to your rule.'

Encouraging your partner to stand firm on their boundaries shows you're trustworthy. On the other hand, expecting everyone to trust you because you're a good person makes you look like exactly the opposite. It's not okay to expect others to feel unsafe, for the benefit of your ego. Remember, you're a stranger to them—a bit of caution is understandable.

Being mindful of safety—yours and others—is a useful skill, not a failsafe. Sometimes people treat us badly, regardless of our precautions. When they do, it's not our fault. But if staying aware can even occasionally help you avoid a risky situation, it's well worth putting these skills into practice.

TL;DR
- Connection is the number one sex move.
- In the long run, being an asshole ruins hook ups for everyone.
- Honesty is a game-changer—and it makes you look confident.

- Safety: it's not just for girls. Even if it's not 100% effective, physical and emotional safety strategies are useful.
- Support your partner's safety as well as your own.

If you've followed along with me in this chapter, you now possess the dating equivalent of a 350-horsepower engine. You can become the kind of person other folks want to get naked with, by being respectful and switched on rather than mean and manipulative. No shady pickup tricks! You have a better way.

Using respect and honesty when picking up is a radical idea, even in these post-#metoo times. I believe it's not only advisable, but essential. As you practice this stuff, hook ups get better and better. Don't take my word for it—try it, if you dare.

Your chance to demonstrate your skills is coming right up, as you meet your next potential playmate...

CHAPTER 6

THE FIRST DATE

What does your perfect hook-up date look like?

Is it a friendly coffee? A few drinks after work? A blow job at your local sex club?

I favour the 'let's have drinks' approach… an opportunity to get to know someone, but not long enough to waste everyone's time, if we turn out to be wrong for each other.

Sometimes I get creative, with hilarious results. I once invited a Tinder match on a walk, because he'd written on his profile that he liked the outdoors. Unfortunately, his idea of outdoors was a drink in the sunshine, while mine was a three-kilometre hike. By the time I'd walked him through a few klicks of bushland, he looked distinctly worse for wear. Just for the record, I still got laid… and we joke about it now.

Whatever your approach, this is the time when all your attitudes and social skills are on display. Swiping on someone's duck face selfie is easy. Charming them is much more difficult.

This chapter will show you how to connect with new people. If you both get along, you can progress from being virtual strangers to a friendship that's the starting point for further sexual exploration.

As well as charming them, you also need to be working out if they're safe, figuring out if they're right for you, and establishing a connection that goes beyond the casual. If everything goes well, you'll then need to negotiate the hook up. These steps are not linear; they happen together. This is why meeting new people is so stressful—we're putting ourselves through serious mental gymnastics. Your date will be struggling with this stuff too.

Remember that number-one sex move we talked about? Connection is key. Connection will get you dates and, if the circumstances are right for both of you, connection will get you laid. Getting to know someone before sex is like stretching before a hike… if you skip it, you're going fall apart halfway through. We're not designed to run before we walk. Here's how to get off to a great start.

CRAFTING THE PERFECT OPENER

So, you've matched with someone online, or found someone in real life that seems your type. What do you say?

And why do you have to say anything, if you know they want a hook up too? Can't you skip the pleasantries and get straight to the sex? Well, not really. If you want to hook up with the right people, conversation is essential. Sex is a vulnerable activity, and whoever you meet will doubtless have encountered a few assholes already; talking demonstrates that you're trustworthy and starts the all-important process of connection.

The bad news is, I'm not a pickup artist. I can't promise a perfect success rate. Once you meet someone that seems right for you, it's your personality (and theirs) that determine whether you decide to go further.

I don't encourage anyone to fake confidence or memorise pickup lines, because other people often smell the bullshit. Cheap tricks and gimmicks are like a thin coat of paint on your backyard fence: it doesn't look good for long.

Blogger and motivational coach Mark Manson is famous for his books, *The Subtle Art of not giving a F*ck* and *Everything is F*cked*. But he also has a lesser-known masterpiece called *Models: Attract Women Through Honesty*. Although it's written in the style of a traditional pickup manual, it offers more than just a quick fix. The book's key message is that we only appeal to potential partners when we genuinely become better people. Manson writes:

I could sell you the best 100 things I've ever said to women, but I can't ever sell you my intentions or my confidence in myself. You must develop those on your own.

He's right. Faking it doesn't work. To connect effectively, you need to practise until you find a way that's genuine. Perhaps you're the type of person who can just crack a few jokes and get everyone laughing; if so, use that. Being good at banter is wonderful, but I've never had the knack. I simply take an interest in others, and trust that honest conversation will lead us toward intimacy.

Here are a few approaches I've found helpful when starting a conversation with a potential match.

GIVE THEM SOMETHING TO WORK WITH

To get along with someone, I need more than just finding them physically attractive; I need to know whether we have anything in common. The introductory chat is make-or-break time, and it's going to be an awkward two minutes if they're not interested in my sci-fi books and I'm not wowed by their love of badminton.

It's helpful if you have something in your profile text that gives me clues, or something in your photos that isn't just you at your mate's wedding. After a certain number of group selfies and duck face, everyone starts to look the same. Why not show a pic of your three dogs, that metal gig you went to last week, or a hobby you're into? Anything to get us talking.

Otherwise, we'll be scraping the bottom of the barrel for interesting conversation right from the start, and that's a bad sign. I have been known to send this message: 'Look, you seem cute, but I have NO idea what to use as an opening line, because your photos don't give me any clues! Help, I'm stuck!' This is funny (to me, at least) and sometimes it works. Sometimes, it doesn't.

My friend Brody hates when people don't post face photos or profile descriptions online. She says, 'When I see a profile without a face, it's impossible for me to feel connection with that person. And if there's no text in their profile, I have no idea whether we'll get along. Having an empty profile is all take, no give. That person gets to see everyone else's stuff, but they aren't willing to put themselves out there. That feels selfish to me. I don't want to talk to someone that hasn't made an effort.'

USE OPEN QUESTIONS, NOT CLOSED QUESTIONS

Imagine you're interviewing a celebrity (I like to imagine it's Chris Hemsworth.) The cameras are rolling and you're sweating under the studio lights. The studio audience are leaning forward in their seats. It's time to get the interview started.

But there's a problem—you haven't prepared any questions. Your interview subject is looking at you expectantly. You need to think fast.

You clear your throat. 'Uh, do you enjoy being an actor?' you say.

'Yes,' they reply.

Silence. Awkwardness. Five seconds after asking, you're right back where you started.

This is a problem every journalist faces. When interviewing people, there are two types of questions that can be asked: closed questions and open questions. Closed questions invite a short response, usually a 'yes' or 'no.' 'Do you like ice cream?' or 'What sort of car do you drive?' These are a bad choice because they don't invite the other person to share much about themselves. Closed questions are conversational dead ends.

OPEN QUESTION: A question that requires more than just a one-word answer.

An open question invites a long, detailed response. For example: 'I'd love to know how your love for passionfruit gelato got started,' or, 'tell me about your last road trip!' Open questions tend to begin with the same sorts of phrases:

- 'Tell me about…'
- 'How did you come to be…'
- 'How do you feel about…'
- 'What's your opinion on…'
- 'How did you…'
- 'What's it like to…'

For initial flirtations, open questions are the way to go. The more conversational goodness you can encourage someone to share, the better your chance of building a connection. Hiding somewhere in that convo will be the gems that you can relate to—the stuff where you can say, 'Wow! I totally get that. Something similar happened to me when I was in Mexico, let me tell you the story…' Finding those relatable nuggets is the key to sparking a deeper connection.

BE HONEST ABOUT WHAT YOU WANT

As I've already discussed, radical honesty is a total game-changer. And it starts here, in the way you represent yourself and how honestly you answer questions like, 'what are you looking for?' It's best if the 'what are you looking for' question comes up before you go on a date with someone. Otherwise, you might waste a whole evening chatting them up, to discover that they only want a serious romantic relationship. Not being honest is a waste of their time, too.

Decoding what people mean is often like being a private detective. Folks never say, 'I'm looking for casual sex.' For some reason it's often referred to as 'fun.'

THE FIRST DATE 111

'I'm not looking for anything serious, just fun.'

'I'm hoping to find people I can have fun with.'

'Wanting to have some fun.'

'Just looking for some fun tonight.'

This is sex-negativity getting us down; talking about sex openly is a no-no, right? We keep falling back on the word 'fun'… or, worse, 'Netflix and chill.' When someone is afraid to be honest with me about wanting to hook up, their unspoken motives make me uneasy. Being direct shows confidence—and confidence is damn sexy.

Of course, it's possible to go too far. Sometimes, when we give ourselves permission to use the word 'sex,' we get totally carried away. Instead of saying, 'I'm just looking for fun, casual sex with the right person,' we end up somewhere south of, 'I'd love to fuck you so hard your eyeballs pop out of your skull.' Not sexy, not appropriate. Keep it casual.

USEFUL LINES
- 'I want to find awesome people to hook up with.'
- 'I'm not looking for a relationship, just a friend to get sexy with sometimes.'
- 'I'm hoping to find the right person for a one-night-stand tonight.'

Notice the use of 'awesome people,' 'a friend,' 'the right person,' etc. Make it clear you have criteria. Otherwise you're basically screaming, 'I just wanna fuck someone! Anyone?' Nobody wants to hang out with a date who doesn't give a rat's ass who they sleep with. Which brings us to the next point…

MAKE SURE THEY'RE RIGHT FOR YOU

Suppose you've found someone appealing and you're having an engaging chat about their dog or their love of hang-gliding or whatever. You might be feeling ready to say, 'Want to continue this discussion over a beer?' but hold up a moment. Read the next bit first.

Dan Savage is an American writer and sex columnist who has given advice on sex and dating for over twenty years. Savage uses the phrase 'dickful thinking' to describe the state people get into where their horniness completely overrides the reality of the situation. It can happen when you have a crush on someone and you're convinced they feel the same, even though they've never shown any sign. But it can also happen when you're so caught up in hopeful fantasies of a glorious night together, that you don't notice someone is completely wrong for you.

If we work from the assumption that bad sex equals wasted time and being treated badly by your date is worse than no date at all, then it's useful to ensure someone is right for you before you smoosh your private parts against theirs.

This is why conversation matters. It's a chance to sound someone out and ensure they're worth spending more time with. With interest - not judgement - observe your potential partner and think, 'Are they a good match for me?'

USEFUL QUESTIONS
- Is this person actually interested? Why not ask them? Anything less than an enthusiastic 'yes,' is a 'no.'
- Are they treating you with respect and consideration?
- Are they looking for the same kind of encounter as you?
- Do you have anything in common, apart from the fact that you both want sex?

Sometimes you find someone who doesn't meet your requirements, but you feel tempted to proceed anyway and see what happens. Hey, I'm not going to tell you 'no.' If you want to, go for it… and afterwards, ask yourself how it turned out. Once you've picked the wrong people a few times, I suspect you'll prefer to wait for the right ones.

HOW TO MAKE A CONNECTION

Let's revisit some material we covered in the 'pre-date flirting' stage.

1. **Find something interesting about your date** and ask them about it.
2. **Use open questions**, not closed questions.
3. **Go deeper**—if you find a mutually interesting topic, explore it!

Intimacy is assumed to be this mysterious force beyond our control. That's the reason we see capital 'L' Love as such a big deal. Feelings are tricky, and if they happen, it feels like magic.

My work in the sex industry has taught me that building trust and intimacy is NOT mysterious. It's a concrete social process, one that you can be aware of, and even cultivate. In a job where winning trust is essential, I've developed the knack for getting folks to bare it all—literally and figuratively.

Dr Arthur Aron, a scientist in the USA, researched intimacy with his study 'The Experimental Generation of Human Closeness'. He asked heterosexual guy/girl pairs to share a series of increasingly personal questions with one another. The experiment aimed to learn whether intimate connections between strangers could be artificially engineered.

The process worked. It worked so well, in fact, that one of the test couples was later married. There you have it - science shows that it's possible to have some control over the process of connection. I'm not trying to get you married, of course—we're talking about hook ups. But a good connection— trust and intimacy—is an essential part of the experience.

The scientific study used a list of thirty-six questions. If you're interested, you can check out the questions online (I've included a web link to them at the end of this book). I find that memorising questions or making a partner read off a list is too predictable; it reminds me of pickup artists and their bad one-liners. What I do, is practise a game called Question and Answer (Q&A).

Q&A was introduced to me by Curious Creatures, a provider of self-development and sexuality workshops in my hometown of Melbourne, Australia. The game has proved so successful in my social circle that we play it whenever we get together—it's a great way to get to know each other! For our purposes, the way I'm describing the game is restricted to two people… although it works just as well for three, five, or ten.

I start by asking, 'Want to play Q&A?' Or if I'm trying to be casual, I say, 'Can I ask you a random personal question? You can ask one too.' If I get an enthusiastic 'yes,' we're good to begin.

HOW TO PLAY 'Q&A'

1. Player One asks a question, e.g., 'What's your favourite colour, and why is it your favourite?'

2. Player Two answers the question: 'Green, because I love hiking and seeing all the different shades of green in the trees. How about you?'

3. Player One answers their own question: 'Black, because it means I never have to worry about my shirt and shoes matching.' (True story.)

4. Now it's Player Two's turn to ask a question: 'Tell me about a time you got into trouble at school...'

5. And so on.

Q&A allows us to talk about the interesting stuff that might not come up in casual conversation. Here are some tips for having the best possible experience:

- **Take an interest in the person, not just their genitals.** Topics must be appropriate—it's not an opportunity to collect sexy stories for your wank-bank. The spirit of the game lies in encouraging someone to trust you and reveal themselves to you. That won't happen if you try to force the conversation in an uncomfortable direction. Sometimes when I say, 'ask me anything!' my partner blurts out the one thing that was on their minds, such as 'do you fuck a lot of guys you've only just met?' Questions like this are self-serving: I can immediately tell they're only interested in getting laid. That's a huge turnoff. If you honestly can't think of anything to ask, it's okay to say, 'pass' or, 'Sorry, I don't want to play this game,' in true radical honesty fashion

- **Keep questions open, not closed.** 'Tell me about', 'how did you', 'what do you think of', etc. The aim is to get a long, detailed answer that allows your partner to be open with you. This will also give you more to talk about. If they say, 'I love the colour green because it reminds me of hiking,' you can reply with 'I love hiking too, what are your fave spots?' There's no shame in having a long conversation between questions—that's the whole idea.

- **Avoid dangerous questions.** Asking, 'What's the worst thing that's ever happened to you?' can go horribly wrong. If your date's response is heavy, you might not be prepared for the story. You might also find them getting upset because you've just reminded them of something traumatic. I once asked a guy 'What's the scariest thing you've ever experienced?' I thought I'd get a fun story about skydiving or something... As it turned out, he had nearly been abducted once while hitchhiking. He felt uncomfortable sharing the story and afterwards we agreed that we shouldn't have gone there.

- **Be a good listener.** Taking turns means giving someone space to speak their story. Minimal words like 'okay' are fine, but if you find yourself jumping in with your own story before they are finished, it's a sign you're not listening as well as you should. Also, if you're just using the time your partner is speaking to think of what you're going to say next, they'll know you're not paying attention.

By gradually moving to deeper topics, you can encourage intimacy. I like to start with something easy such as, 'What would your perfect vacation look like?' As the date progresses, personal questions may become more appropriate, e.g., 'Tell me about something in your life that makes you feel happy.' With practice, you'll start to get an idea of the questions to ask next. But remember that either of you can pass on a question, if you're not comfortable answering.

HOW DO WE KNOW IF THERE'S A CONNECTION?

Working out what other people think is really fucking hard.

Pickup artists discuss this a lot. They recommend paying attention to someone's eye contact, their body language, or how often they touch you, to guess whether they are interested in sex.

Some folks think that talking openly about sexy stuff means the date is going in a sexual direction. But bringing up the topic can go super wrong, if you've misjudged the situation. I once had a guy, in the first five minutes of our date, tell me that he was into extreme kink. I'm kinky too, but his starting a discussion about sex so fast felt creepy and it caused me to doubt his social skills. It's worth waiting a while, and getting some feedback, before you start talking about sexy specifics.

When I'm trying to work out if things are going well, I pay attention to the feelings in my body. If I'm feeling relaxed, and want to be closer to them, it's a good sign. If I feel uneasy or sense distance, I ask myself why. I give it time—wait until a couple of hours have gone by, or until they have made a move first.

If all the signals are looking good and you're sure there's interest, then it's time to use your words and ask them… in a sexy, radically honest way, because that's how we do things around here.

USEFUL LINES

- 'I reckon there's a bit of a connection here, is that right?'
- 'I sort of feel like there's a sexy vibe right now—am I getting that right?'
- 'Wow, I think you're pretty awesome. How are you feeling about this date so far?'

It's essential to give them space to let you know how they feel. Although checking in is nerve-wracking, it's better than getting the signals wrong.

Asking first, and thereby demonstrating your confidence, makes you look badass. Going in for a kiss and having someone recoil… not so much.

HOW TO NEGOTIATE A HOOK UP

The conversation is flowing, the vibe is sexy. You've asked your date, and they think things are going well too. What happens next?

This is where the radical honesty comes in handy. Now is the time when you're going to feel the most temptation to let go of the steering wheel and just let things happen. If he starts making out with you, or she invites you back to her place, it might feel awkward to stop and have 'the conversation.'

But this groundwork is necessary. The aim of a good hook up is to leave everyone feeling positive. You need to set up expectations, otherwise everything is likely to blow up in your face once you've finished having sex—or it might even blow up earlier, if you haven't communicated properly and you've misunderstood whether someone is interested in getting sexy at all.

Timing is crucial. There's no point getting stuck into the 'let's fuck' conversation before you've ordered your first beer. I like to wait until the end of the night, until I'm sure there's sexual chemistry. And I ask first: 'I feel like we have a good connection, are you feeling it too?'

Then we get to the difficult bit. For me, it goes like this:

1. A question about my partner's needs: 'What would you like to get out of this?'

2. Being clear on what I want: 'I'm not looking for a relationship right now, but I'd love to take you home...'

3. Inviting a yes/no: '... if you think that would be fun?'

USEFUL LINES

- 'I'm getting a vibe that things are going well, is it time for me to invite you home?'
- 'Just to let you know, I'm not looking for romance. But if you'd like to make out/fool around/get it on, I'd love to hang out with you... what do you think?'
- 'I think you're awesome and I'm feeling some chemistry, am I right? What would you like to get up to tonight?'

If you hear a 'no' at this point, how well you handle your rejection will tell your partner what sort of person you are. If you're respectful and take it well, you'll appear strong. If you whinge, get mad, or tell them they're wrong, you'll look like a spoiled child. A 'no' is usually more about the other person than it's about you—they might not be having a great day, you may not be their type, or maybe the connection just didn't happen. Now you know, and you can save your effort for the next potential hook up. It doesn't need to be a big deal.

If your date replies, 'hell yeah!' then you're all set...

TL;DR

- Use open questions for a faster connection.
- Use your initial contact to ensure your new friend is right for you.
- Q&A is the only game you need to know on a first date!
- Not sure if there's a spark? Listen to your intuition... then ask. Until you ask, you can't be sure.

- Do your hook-up negotiations now—don't wait until it's too late.

So far, we've learned how to establish a connection that goes beyond the superficial, and how to judge whether the time is right to take things to the bedroom. These skills are invaluable—once mastered, you'll be able to guide your date in the right direction, without fear of running yourself (or anyone else) off the road.

Now, if you've been given the green light, we can move on to the sexy stuff! Chapter Seven covers essential sex moves for excellent hook ups.

CHAPTER 7

ESSENTIAL SEX MOVES

Here they are: the bare essentials for better sex, pun intended.

Remember sex education classes in high school? If your school was anything like mine, you spent sex-ed watching one of your gym teachers demonstrate how to roll a condom onto a banana and sneaking guilty glances at the anatomical diagrams. If you were lucky, you might have gotten some information on safer sex and why it's important. If you were unlucky, you copped a lecture about premarital sex and why it's bad.

Sex education often focuses on the technicalities—the medical information you need to know, such as the mechanics of intercourse and the dangers of sexually transmitted infections (STIs). The problem with this stuff? It's boring as hell. And it doesn't tell you how to have better sex.

Thank Christ for the Internet. When I was seventeen, I discovered a website called For Unlawful Carnal Knowledge (FUCK). It was put together on a shoestring budget by a few anonymous blokes, solely for the purpose of giving people the sex advice they weren't getting elsewhere. The website covered topics such as oral sex, pubic landscaping, and giving feedback to your partner. In the dark ages of bad sex-ed, it was like a holy light from above.

Alas, you can't trust everything you see on the Net. A quick glance at sites such as PornHub will reveal that not all sex education is created equal— watch too much gonzo porn, and you'll end up with a very unrealistic idea of how sex happens. If porn were true, your best friend's wife would always be down for a threesome, and every guy would have a ten-inch dick. That's not how the world works.

So, who can we trust for reliable information? The idea of asking friends or family for advice might feel terrifying—you're just supposed to know, right? But how? Sex, like anything else, is a learned behaviour. It takes experimentation and practice. The less we talk with each other about it, the more we're left flailing around in the dark (sometimes literally).

I think everyone deserves to have a great sex life. I can't make it happen— only you can—but I can certainly provide some useful information. This knowledge comes from my years as a sex worker, kinkster, and hook-up addict.

Seeing sex as a mysterious process that we can't control means we often don't think about the practicalities. It's a convenient excuse for cheating on your romantic partner or forgetting to use condoms: 'We got carried away!' It's also used as a shitty excuse for hurting other people. Most significantly, being 'carried away' means we get to excuse ourselves from the feelings of shame we associate with sex. We sometimes try to deny responsibility. We dodge our shame around sex by pretending we're 'out of control'.

There are two problems with this attitude:

1. Making excuses for your actions is a cop-out.
2. If you get carried away, you fall back on doing whatever seems familiar, and the sex will be boring.

Good sex happens when everyone is concentrating on what they're doing. I can't make it happen for you, but I can provide the information that you need, once you decide to put your hands on the steering wheel. The following chapter details essential sex skills for a great encounter: using consent for amazing connection, switching up the script so you never get bored, and becoming a safer sex pro.

Sex is the meat in the sandwich of a good hook up… and, like making a sandwich, hook ups are boring if we do them the same way every time. Let's elevate your experience to the gourmet level.

HOW TO DO CONSENT (WITHOUT LOOKING LIKE A LOSER)

You might wonder why we're still talking about consent, right after you ask your date if they want to get sexy. Consent means making sure someone agrees to sex, right? They just did that, so why are we still worrying about it?

Lots of folks assume that consent is something you ask for once, before you forge ahead like a Spartan soldier. Others reckon it's a buzz-kill—they're afraid of being that loser who says, 'may I kiss you?' Or it goes the other way—we assume it's the other person's job to get consent, and not ours.

The #metoo movement is changing that. It shows that fucking up consent happens more often than we realise, and that it has nasty repercussions for both the victim and the perpetrator. #metoo also has a lot of folks running scared, because they're afraid of being criticised for not knowing how to do consent. That's not my beef. I'm not going to shame you by saying you're a bad person if you don't do consent the same way I do. I understand that most of the world doesn't get why it's important, and most people don't think about consent much during their sexual encounters.

Here's what I think: consent is something we're all entitled to—it's good to know your human rights. Consent is also an amazing tool for having better sex.

THE BASICS: CONSENT IS A HUMAN RIGHT

To understand consent, you need to understand boundaries.

BOUNDARIES: Rules you make about your needs and how you want to be treated.

In our lives, there are certain things that we have the right to control. These include our bodies, our immediate space, our thoughts, and our feelings. If you check out the diagram on the opposite page, you'll see that all this—what I call 'your stuff'—falls within your personal boundaries. Nobody has a right to control your stuff. Nobody has a right to tell you what to do with your body, what to eat, where to go, or what opinions to have.

When it comes to boundaries, society is pretty fucked up. Our parents, teachers, friends, and bosses often pressure us to do things we don't want. We're made to kiss relatives on the cheek when we're kids, pressured to drink with our mates when we're trying to quit, and told to 'man up' when we're sad. This is why we suck at consent—we're so used to other people invading our boundaries, that we barely notice the boundaries of others.

YOUR PERSONAL BOUNDARIES

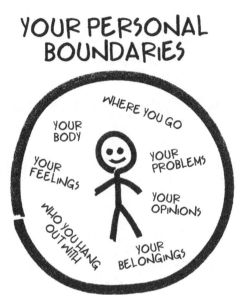

When our stuff isn't under our control, we feel sad, scared, and fucked up. Being good at consent means being aware of your own boundaries, and other people's boundaries, and respecting everyone's right to be themselves. This is why asking before getting sexy is so important - we all have a right to our personal boundaries.

THE ADVANCED MOVES: CONSENT AS A TOOL FOR BETTER SEX

Consent doesn't just stop sexual assault. Consent is a tool that makes sex way, way better. When you understand how to use this, you'll become an incredible lover.

First things first—what happens when one person's boundaries get smooshed up against someone else's during a sexual encounter? We end up with something like this:

BOUNDARIES FOR HOOK-UPS
(NOT JUST DURING SEX, THE WHOLE DATE)

YOUR STUFF

THEIR STUFF

↑ CONSENT

When you're hooking up with someone, you both need to negotiate the overlap between your stuff and their stuff. If you kiss someone, they need to want to kiss you too. If they get all kinky on your ass, they need to ensure you're down for that. Not just physical stuff, either. If you want to 'Netflix & chill' and you put on a horror movie, you both need to be okay with seeing zombies.

> **CONSENT:** Enthusiastic agreement to do something - beforehand, and while it's happening.

As I said before, most of us aren't used to being honest. We try to guess what other people think, and then if someone complains afterwards, we shrug and say, 'Sorry, I thought you liked zombies'. For good sex, that doesn't cut it. To ensure that it's good for everyone, you must ask while it's happening.

A lot of folks think doing consent means asking, 'is this okay?' every thirty seconds. That's not how a sexpert does it. I hate 'Is this okay?' in the middle of fucking. Not because my partner is a loser for asking—I appreciate the concern. But it's super unhelpful, for two reasons:

1. They are already doing the thing when they ask about it… if I'm upset, it's too late.
2. 'Okay' is a low bar to set, don't you think?

I don't want the sex you have to be 'okay'; it should be amazing. If you're having sex with someone and they say 'Look, this is okay, but I'm sort of bored and I'd rather just watch television' then of course you'll feel bad—what's sexy about that? If you're not getting off on your partner's enjoyment, then why bother having them around at all? Both your partner's pleasure and your own are important. This is 'enthusiastic consent': not just 'yes' but 'Oh, God, yes, don't stop, you feel amazing!'

Here's how I do consent, both in my work as an escort and my personal life. If you think consent kills the mood, you're about to find out otherwise…

HOW TO DO CONSENT LIKE A PRO

1. GET CONSENT BEFORE YOU DO SOMETHING

… without making it weird and awkward. It's not about saying 'can I x your y?' every minute. It's about showing your intentions—moving in to kiss them gradually so they have time to say no, for example. You should also ask, but there are sexy ways to do it.

Player One: 'I'd love to put my arms around you right now.'

Player Two: 'I want that too.'

You might ask for directions, if your partner is good at communicating. Perhaps they've read this book and they know how to be radically honest? Try:

Player One: 'How do you want to be touched right now?'

Player Two: 'I'd love you to pull my hair.'

Player One: 'I'm up for that...'

Note that just asking isn't enough. Ask... pause... and listen for an 'enthusiastic yes'. Anything less than clear, 'yes!' is a 'no'.

Do you have to ask before every little thing? Lots of people don't like consent because they think it means having to sign off on a list of every possible activity before the fun starts—which sounds pretty fucking awkward.

Sometimes it's essential to ask, and sometimes you need to use your judgement. I always ask before physical contact with someone new ('I'd love to put my arms around you right now'), doing anything that involves orifices ('Can I put my fingers inside you?') or anything that might be painful or surprising ('How do you feel about hair pulling?') Sometimes I get a hunch that my partner is nervous; if that happens, I take more care to ask. As I get to know someone, we trust each other more and talk less. But I'll still ask every now and again, to demonstrate that a 'no' is always welcome even if we're doing something familiar.

2. CHECK IN AS YOU DO SOMETHING

This is where the magic happens. Instead of 'just doing the sex' and desperately hoping they like it... slow down, look them in the eye and ask, 'How does that feel?'

This line is useful for complicated stuff such as giving head or making someone cum. Rather than having to guess, you can listen to their feedback and adjust your technique until you get it right.

Player One: 'How does this feel?'

Player Two: 'Yeah, fine.'

Player One: 'Just fine? How could we make it better?'

Player Two: 'Maybe a bit faster?'

Player One: 'Like this?'

Player Two: *'OH MY GOD YES.'*

3. DEBRIEF AFTERWARDS

Talking about what you've both just done allows you to enjoy the afterglow. It also addresses all those little post-sex insecurities: do they still like you? Did you do okay?

Player One: 'How was that for you?'

Player Two: 'Good, except that bit where I kicked you in the head when I came. Sorry about that.'

Player One: 'No worries, I'm fine.'

Player Two: 'How was the sex, though?'

Player One: 'It was great!'

Communicating during sex almost feels like cheating. You have a direct line to someone's needs and desires. No more guessing. Only asking. More connection, more orgasms, less angst. What's not to love?

THE EASY WAY: TRAFFIC LIGHT SAFE WORDS

I understand that, for a lot of people, talking about sex can be difficult. If mid-coitus discussion isn't your style, the traffic light safe word system is a quick-n-dirty alternative.

> **SAFE WORD:** A pre-arranged code word used to signal how you're feeling...or stop everything.

Safe words are code words designed to signal consent. They are often used by people who do kinky stuff, as a way to stop everything in an emergency. But safe words work well for regular sex too. Rather struggling to find the right words, you can use ones you've already agreed on with your partner.

The traffic light system uses three safe words: green, orange, and red.

- 'Green' means, 'Yes, this is great! Keep going!'
- 'Orange' means, 'I don't like this specific activity' or 'I've reached my limit, you need to slow down.'
- 'Red' means, 'Everything must stop now!'

For this system to be effective, everyone needs to agree on how it works. Explaining safe words to new play partners is simple, once you know what you're talking about. Here's how the conversation goes for me:

Player One: 'Want to come back to my place?

Player Two: 'Yeah!'

Player One: 'Just to let you know, I use traffic light safe words.'

Player Two: 'What's that?'

Player One: 'They're code words we can use so we know everything's okay. Green means you're doing great. Orange means that something doesn't feel good and needs adjusting. Red means everything has to stop.'

Player Two: 'Oh… uh, okay.'

Player One: 'So… are you green to come home with me?'

Player Two: 'I'm green!'

Player One: (three hours later) 'Are you still green?'

Player Two: 'GREEN!'

If shouting colours during sex seems weird to you, I assure you it quickly becomes normal. Like being honest, it gets easier as you practise. I love doing something to a partner that makes them shout 'Green!' at the top of their lungs. My neighbours think we're nuts, but that's a small price to pay.

USEFUL LINES
- 'Still green?'… 'Yep!'
- 'Orange on the hair pulling.'… 'Oh, thanks for letting me know.'
- 'I'm SO green for what you're doing right now…'
- 'Red!'… 'Are you okay?'… 'No, I just got a cramp!'
- 'Green for dirty talk?'… 'Yeah, green!'… 'Awesome.'

Using traffic light safe words means you don't have to agonise over what to say in the moment, because you already have words prepared. Thus, it's easier to ask… and easier to speak up.

'WHAT IF I FUCK UP CONSENT?'

Consent isn't that hard, but it might feel unfamiliar. If you're like me, nobody has ever taught you how to do it. All we have is trial and error… it's inevitable that we fuck up from time to time.

WAYS WE FUCK UP CONSENT

- **Not being specific enough**—'He said he liked rough sex, so I thought it was okay to slap him in the face.'

- **Mistaking a 'maybe' for a 'yes'**—sometimes, if we're keen, we hear a 'maybe' as an enthusiastic yes. But for good consent, a 'maybe' is a no. If you hear a mixed message, stop and ask for more information.

- **Forgetting we need to ask**—there are lots of things that we are so used to doing, we forget they're things that need consent. Touching someone, for example, or giving them a hug. Pregnant women complain about strangers touching their bellies—this is just one of the ways we accidentally touch people without their permission.

- **Power imbalance**—there are times when a person's 'yes' is less valid, such as if they're scared of you or if you have power over them (e.g., the aforementioned 'boss hitting on you' example). If you have reason to believe your partner can't safely say 'no', you need to back away.

- **Inability to consent**—if your partner is drunk, high or under the age of consent then they may be unable to consent to sex (no matter what they say). Going ahead in this situation is unwise—it could be considered sexual assault or statutory rape, depending on the circumstances. Not to mention, it's an asshole move.

- **Becoming distracted**—as we discussed earlier, there's this idea that good sex means getting totally carried away, and not bothering with pesky stuff like safer sex or consent. I call bullshit on this. But it's true that sometimes, in the heat of the moment, we forget our sex skills. If you realise you've dropped the ball, stop and check in with your partner immediately: 'How are you feeling right now?'

- **Withholding information**—sometimes we might hide information from our partners that would stop us from getting laid, if only they knew. The classic example is letting your partner think you're in love with them, when you just want sex. But it also includes behaviour such as stealthing (taking the condom off halfway through sex and hoping they don't notice). Withholding info if you know your partner wouldn't consent otherwise is a form of sexual assault.

- **Not stopping when the 'yes' stops**—sometimes folks freak out during sex or freeze up. Sometimes they're not having fun but don't know how to tell you. If you don't get an enthusiastic 'yes' at any point, you need to stop and make sure everything is still good.

- **Assuming you don't have to ask**. Some people say, 'I don't need to ask, because I can just tell it's ok.' Some people say, 'It's the guy's job to ask.' Sometimes this approach will work—but sometimes it won't. People can, and do, get hurt; girls, guys, whoever. If you violate someone's consent, 'I assumed I didn't need to ask' doesn't cut it. Consent is something everyone needs to think about.

If you've fucked up, it might be obvious right away—or you might work it out later, if your partner confronts you or you start to have second thoughts.

It feels bad when we realise we've hurt someone else, intentional or not. What do you do if you find yourself in this situation?

- **Listen**. You might feel defensive, especially if it was an accident. You might have the urge to say, 'But I didn't mean to!' or 'Why are you giving me a hard time?' You might feel angry. The thing to remember is, the person you've violated deserves to have their feelings heard. It's important that you behave in a way that allows them to feel safe. It doesn't matter whether your mistake was large or small. It doesn't matter whether it was accidental or intentional. This is about them, not you—they need to be listened to.

- **Accept that everyone makes mistakes.** If you genuinely didn't mean to hurt them, then you're not a terrible person. People of all genders fuck up consent and live to tell the tale. The crucial thing is the next step...

- **Own your actions like a boss.** Take responsibility. Stand up and say, 'I did that.' Ask your partner what you can do to make amends. And—most importantly—ask yourself what you need to do to avoid making the same mistake in the future. Consent fuck-ups are valuable because they help us become better people.

Getting consent right is something everyone needs to work on; not just to avoid hurting others, but also to improve the quality of the connection we have with our partners. Doing consent like a pro gives you the information you need to protect the people you care about (including yourself) and to be the best lover you can be.

AVOID BORING SEX...
DITCH THE SCRIPT

Here's where we're at: you now have powerful tools to keep yourself and your playmates safe. You understand the value of being the best person you can be. Armed with this knowledge, we can now make things interesting. It's time to change the script.

During hetero, two-person sexual encounters, many folks default to a standard way of doing things. This is the standard script of nearly every movie sex scene or porn clip we've ever watched. It goes something like:

1. Kissing;
2. Foreplay (touching and stuff);
3. Oral sex;
4. PIV (penis-in-vagina) sex;
5. Guy cums, game over.

(If you're lucky, you might add an extra step: Girl cums. But this doesn't happen as often.)

When hetero folks think about sex, they often focus mainly on PIV intercourse. The end goal is for the guy to get off—it's a race to the finish line. But rushing to PIV, and treating everything else as unimportant, often results in boring, predictable sex. When it's only about orgasms, we neglect all the other fun stuff.

I believe that sex is about more than just orifices. Sex is about everything— the look you give someone over a glass of wine before you take them home, their arm around your waist in the lift, the way they kiss, the way they touch. Sex is all the things you do with someone before intercourse, and the stuff you do afterwards. Sex isn't a few moments of PIV: it's the whole package.

When I talk about going off script, I mean letting go of the timeline and making room for experiments. Going off script means spending three hours making out, if that's what you want to do. It means stopping halfway through fucking and giving someone a massage for a while. It means doing oral sex but not PIV sex, or hand jobs instead of oral sex. Most importantly, means working out what you REALLY want, rather than just following along with what you think you SHOULD be doing.

The best sex happens when we're focused on our experience and our lovers' bodies. Often, when we follow a standard script, that awareness is switched off. It's like watching a classic movie: it's a familiar story, so you don't concentrate on what's happening. When I do this in front of the TV, I sometimes can't even remember how the show ended.

This might be fine during a re-run of *Titanic* but forgetting to pay attention during sex is a real tragedy. Not only will you enjoy yourself less, your partner will notice the difference too.

When we ditch the script, we focus. Suddenly you need to switch on, communicate with your partner, and pay attention to make sure they're enjoying themselves. This means being one-hundred percent present in your sexual encounter. It's a mental trick—you're forcing your brain to wake up and enjoy what's happening. Meditation enthusiasts call this 'mindfulness.'

> **MINDFULNESS:** Being totally aware of what you're sensing, feeling, and doing.

Have you ever kissed someone and immediately forgotten about anything else that's going on? I'm referring to those amazing make out sessions where you could be in the middle of the street stopping traffic, and you wouldn't notice the car horns or people screaming at you through their rolled-down windows. Similarly, good sex makes you forget about everything except what's happening in the moment. That's what being switched on is all about.

HOW TO GO OFF SCRIPT

Ditching the script requires initiative. Your partner probably assumes the sex is going to be the same as usual. When you ask if you can cover them in baby oil or spend five minutes kissing the back of their neck, they'll be surprised. I've found that once I've suggested it, most folks are keen to try something different.

No matter how experienced you are, it takes experimentation to find out what works. This is what our consent language is for—making sure your lover agrees and continually improving your technique based on their feedback. Everyone enjoys different techniques; that amazing move where you lick the inside of someone's elbow might be a total downer for the next person. Over time you'll build up a repertoire of techniques that often work for you. But remember to ask before you pull something new out of your 'sex moves' toolbox.

OFF-SCRIPT IDEAS

- **Slow down**—it's easy to rush when you're nervous. Remember that the sex is about whatever you're doing NOW, not about trying to get somewhere in a hurry. Everyone benefits, both psychologically and physically, by taking more time. Rushing things robs us of the full experience.

- **Make eye contact**—when we're nervous and distracted, we often forget to acknowledge our partners. Losing that feeling of connection can destroy a sexual encounter. On the other hand, making long eye contact is a great way to be present with your lover.

- **Take turns giving and receiving**—rather than just having a free-for-all. It's difficult to concentrate on the sensations of sex when we're busy attending to someone else. It's also hard to do a good job when we're distracted—for example, by our partner trying to get us off too. The way to escape this issue is to take turns—let your partner do things for you or encourage them to relax while you do things for them. Then swap over. Some folks have trouble with this because they feel uncomfortable being the centre of attention ('What if he's tired of giving me head?') or they feel nervous when they're expected to perform for someone else ('What if I'm not doing this right? Fuck!'). The way to short-circuit the anxiety is to communicate using the skills you've just learned.

- **Try new things that aren't just 'kiss', 'oral sex' or 'fuck.'** Sex is usually very genital-focused because we assume that orgasm is the only goal. We go straight for the junk and neglect the rest of our partners' bodies. There are lots of ways to touch someone that don't involve their clit, nipples or cock: you could run your hands over their body (varying the speed and pressure) or try kissing them in different places (back of the neck is a good place to start).

- **Hold, grasp, squeeze**—put your hands around someone's waist or wrap yourself around them and enjoy how their body feels in your arms. Keep it gentle, unless you've specifically negotiated otherwise. Rough manipulation, grabbing, and holding counts as 'kinky shit', and you need some extra skills to do that safely (which are covered in the advanced section of this book).

- **Vary the pace**—if you're fucking someone, try slowing right down. If you've been going slow and romantic, try speeding up momentarily. Varying the speed creates intense sensations.

- **Get off the bed**—try the couch, the floor, the shower, or in front of your hall mirror. It's hard to stick to the script while you're trying to balance on the edge of a kitchen bench! Anything that changes up the normal routine will force you to think creatively.

- **Massage**—enough said. Few people refuse a back or shoulder massage (although of course you still need to check in that they want it). I'm particularly fond of head massages—I've found it has a whole-body-orgasm effect on some of my lovers. A real sexpert keeps some massage oil handy (see the 'sex toys' chapter for more information).

- **Dirty talk**—lying in bed talking about what turns you on makes for hot sex. It's not for the shy. But it's a great way to bring up activities you might like to do together.

- **Mutual masturbation**—asking to watch someone else get themselves off is hot. It also gives you a lot of clues about the sort of touch they might enjoy from you later. Again, this won't work for shy people who aren't comfortable with people looking at them. If I'm with a new partner, I'm careful to encourage them and tell them how hot they look so that they feel less nervous.

Lots of folks don't like going off script because they worry that they won't know what to do next, and they'll look silly. When we do only what's expected, we can hide behind social convention. The problem with this approach is that it reduces sex down to its most boring possible form. Instead of doing amazing things to each other, we end up being predictable.

It's okay to try new things even if it means you occasionally mess up. I was once kicked in the head by a lady in the middle of a threesome—it was accidental (and she was embarrassed) but I thought it was hilarious and so did her husband. Should I have skipped the threesome just in case something weird happened? Hell, no!

Good sex involves trial and error. To become amazing, you need to let go of the need to look perfect and 'normal' (which is bullshit, as we've established). Keep reminding yourself that nobody knows how to 'do' sex—we're all just winging it. Trying to pretend you know everything will probably make you look sillier than not caring whether you do or don't. My advice: let go of your fear, skip the boring sex, and put yourself on the path to greatness.

If you're really stuck on how to go off script, perhaps playing a game with your partner might help? Unlike strip poker and 'spin the bottle' - which push people into doing stuff they're not ready for - some sex games allow you to actually ask for what you want. The best of these is called the Two-Minute Game.

The Two-Minute Game is a turn-based game. Each player gives and receives an activity for a short amount of time. The game has been practised and taught in various forms by a variety of sex educators over the years. It's the sex equivalent of speed dating; it allows you to get to know your partner in stages and gives you guidelines to follow, so you never feel lost for what to do.

The version below has been provided by Curious Creatures.

THE TWO-MINUTE GAME

LEARNING GOALS
- Getting good (and quick) at asking for what you want.
- Learning more about what a partner enjoys.
- A little structure helps you focus on your pleasure.
- Play stays balanced, and it keeps you in sync with each other.

HOW TO PLAY

Decide who's going first (Player One).

Player One: checks in with their body and asks for what they want. This can either be something they'd like to receive, or something they'd like to do.

Player Two: accepts the request or offers alternative suggestions— it's fine to negotiate and arrive at something you're both happy with.

Player Two: sets a two-minute timer and begins giving the agreed activity.

When the timer goes off, play stops and Player Two then asks for what they'd like. And repeat. And repeat.

THINGS TO WATCH FOR

It doesn't need to get sexy! Sometimes this is just a lovely way to hang out and connect intimately. Sometimes you'll want to play this for three minutes per turn, or even five minutes. This can be good, however one of the joys of the two-minute length is that the timer will go off before most things reach their 'use by date', for either person. That leaves you with a slight sense of longing, rather than relief that the activity has finished.

Trust your intuition and your body, when it's your turn to ask for what you want. One of the best things about this game is having fun with the slightly unusual, quirky things that people ask for.

Here are some of our favourite things to give or receive:

- Fetching a cup of tea.
- Cradling someone's head in your lap.
- Nipple sucking (as if your life depends on it!)
- Stroking, from ankles to the base of the neck, as slowly as possible.
- 'Tell me what you like about your body, for two minutes.'
- 'Massage my G-spot, for two minutes'

The two-minute game is an incredible tool. It allows your partner and yourself to share giving and receiving equally. And it encourages communication—everybody must speak up and ask for what they want.

When I play with my partners, I use an app on my phone to track the time. We gradually move from kissing and gentle touch all the way up to full-on, mind-blowing sex—all in two-minute intervals.

The trickiest part of the game is teaching it to others. A new date might be hard to convince, if they're used to the regular 'sex on script' approach. Being able to explain the rules confidently is essential - practice on a few of your friends and you'll sound more confident when you're talking with hook-up partners.

The Two-Minute Game isn't for everyone - sometimes it's just too new or unusual, and that's okay. But I often introduce new people to this game; after a few rounds of nervous giggles, my partners usually start to appreciate it.

If you're on the East Coast of Australia, Curious Creatures runs workshops that include the Two-Minute Game. It's helpful to be able to practice it in person, in a supportive environment. You can find out more about Curious Creatures in the Further Reading chapter.

SAFER SEX SECRETS

As an escort, I spend a lot of time showing people how to do safer sex. I sometimes feel like a safer sex expert! Before I was a sex worker, however, I was just a civilian who didn't know any more about this stuff than the average human. Here's the information I wish I'd known earlier.

Safer sex is anything we do to prevent the spread of sexually transmissible infections (STIs). It's called 'safer sex', not 'safe sex' for a reason: all sex involves risk. But with the know-how, you can reduce that risk enormously.

> **SAFER SEX:** Anything you do to avoid catching (or spreading) STIs.

Some people feel that safer sex isn't an issue now that we have HIV/AIDS under control. Sometimes they try to talk their partners into sex without condoms, because it feels better, and they think there isn't much risk. I know that for lots of folks, sex is more fun without barriers. But there's still some bad stuff out there that you should protect yourself from (Google 'antibiotic-resistant gonorrhoea' if you don't believe me). Some STIs that we thought we had beaten, such as chlamydia and syphilis, are becoming a problem again because people aren't taking condom use seriously.

Knowing how to do safer sex isn't just about staying free of STIs. It's also about looking confident, rather than fumbling around every time you need to put on a rubber. There's this idea among the general population that if you look like you know too much, you'll appear too experienced (aka, 'slutty'). This is bullshit. Being a sexpert is damn sexy, regardless of your gender. Anyone who's suspicious of your expertise is suffering from the sex-negative problems we discussed in Part I.

There are lots of ways people do safer sex. I can't tell you the best way; it's up to you to decide what level of risk you're comfortable with. Below is a chart that shows which STIs are easily passed during various sexual activities.

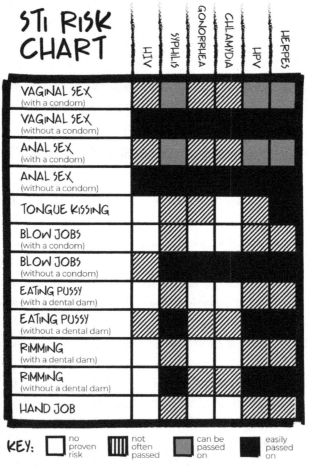

This risk chart is based on data from the BC Center for Disease Control and the Australian Government Department of Health. It's important to do your own research too, as our knowledge of the risks changes over time.

THE FIRST LINE OF DEFENCE: SAFER SEX SUPPLIES

Here are the basic tools at your disposal.

CONDOMS

Condoms are essential for every hook up. These are basically a thin barrier that's designed to go between someone's dick and whomever they put it in. They are used for vaginal and anal sex. Although it's less common, some folks use them for oral sex too, because some STIs can be transmitted in the throat.

Condoms are usually made of latex but are also available in polyurethane (which feels nice and won't give you a bad reaction if you have a latex allergy). They come in a variety of sizes, and you need the correct size for the penis in question, otherwise they may break or fall off mid-sex.

Conventional wisdom dictates that condoms should be worn at all times during penetrative sex, unless you're in a long-term relationship and have had a 'no condoms' discussion, along with appropriate STI tests.

For condoms to work properly you need to pinch the tip before you roll them onto the dick. This creates a bit of space in the end for the cum to occupy, post-orgasm. If you don't do this the jizz escapes, which is messy and risky. Condoms need to be rolled all the way down to the base of the penis. Use them with lubricant—rubber burn is not a fun experience.

After orgasm, the condom must be taken off straight away, because cocks shrink after cumming, and the condom could fall off. Hold on to the base when you withdraw, to make sure it doesn't slip.

THE FEMALE CONDOM, AKA INSERTIVE CONDOM

This little-known beauty fits into and over a pussy or into a butt hole (if you're using it for anal sex). Insertive condoms are useful for smaller penises that condoms don't fit, or for guys who hate the feel of regular condoms but still want to be safe. The insertive condom offers more protection than a regular condom, because it covers more of the pussy/arse (although it does look a little different, because more of the barrier is visible on the outside of your junk.)

Insertive condoms will give a penis-owner more sensation, due to the increased friction. The trade-off is that the wearer will experience less. It's almost as if you're transferring that slight loss of sensitivity from the cock to the pussy/ass—a sacrifice I'm happy to make occasionally, for the sake of my partners' enjoyment!

Insertive condoms are tricky to find, but fun to play with! To find some, try your local sexual health clinic or chemist.

DENTAL DAMS

These are square bits of latex or plastic that are placed between your mouth and someone's ass or pussy when you're going down on them. Realistically, not many hetero folk use them. Hell, not many queer folk use them either. But I do use them—at work, during threesomes—so that I can go down on ladies without worrying about chlamydia and gonorrhoea. Basically, it's your choice. Dental dams are available from chemists and sexual health clinics.

Condoms and dental dams are single use only. Just make sure you throw them in the bin and not in the toilet, because you'll fuck up your plumbing. Then there's one more item…

LUBRICANT (AKA, 'LUBE,' AKA, 'PASS ME THE LUBE!')

Personal lubricant is essential for a good sexual encounter. For PIV there's this weird idea that, if a vagina is aroused, it will automatically get wet and sex will be easy—this might be true for some people, but most of us need assistance. If you're doing another type of sex, such as anal, then you don't have any sort of natural moisture to work with and it's even more important to lube up.

Lube is the difference between enjoyable sex and feeling as though someone is trying to take the top layer of skin off your genitals with a cheese grater. Don't believe what you see in porn; spit doesn't cut it. Lubricant also lessens the risk of a condom break.

There are many types of lube. The most popular is water-based, which washes off easily. I prefer silicone lube because it doesn't dry up as quickly. Silicone lube feels oilier, and is harder to wash off, but also lasts much longer. Be aware that silicone lube can destroy silicone toys… so don't use it with your expensive dildos.

I don't recommend flavoured lubes, because sometimes they have sugar in them, which can mess up vaginas and give them infections. Oil-based lube (such as massage oils) are a bad idea—oil breaks down latex, and will almost inevitably result in a condom break. Never use oil-based lube with latex condoms! If you're giving your lover an oil massage, make sure you wipe them down thoroughly and wash your hands before sex.

BUT... CONDOMS REALLY SUCK?

If you hate the way condoms feel, you're not alone. Some dudes lose sensation, and some have trouble getting hard or cumming during sex. Condoms are most often a problem when you've just come out of a long-term relationship, as this is when you really notice the difference.

Pressuring your playmates into condom-less fucking is NOT the solution. Unsafe sex leaves everyone feeling worse off—either right away or the day after, when anxiety sets in.

CONDOM STRATEGIES THAT WORK

- **Try extra-thin or latex-free condoms.** My fave is Skyn, a non-latex brand that feels really natural. Non-latex condoms have an entirely different sensation: they warm up on your skin readily and often feel softer than the stock-standard options. Check out your chemist—there are lots of varieties available. Shop online if you can't find exactly what you're looking for at your local.

- **Use lube.** Put some lube on the end of your cock before you put the condom on. This increases the level of sensation. You don't want to lube the whole cock, because then the condom will slide off mid-sex and you'll have a safer sex emergency on your hands. If you have a pussy, using plenty of lube on the outside of the condom makes the sensation significantly better.

- **Re-train your brain.** Stop having sex for a while. If you haven't cum recently, you're more likely to cum with a condom on during sex. Alternatively, try masturbating while wearing a condom to help get your cock used to the sensation.

- **Pull out, take the damn thing off and finish with a hand job** if you're having trouble getting to orgasm.

Now that HIV/AIDS is considered manageable, some folks are giving up on safer sex entirely. Barebacking (having sex without barrier protection) sometimes happens because people judge the risk to be acceptably low. It's true that the risk is low, but it's growing—occurrences of STIs are on the rise, because folks aren't practising safer sex as often as they should. It's a bit like being an asshole: you might get away with it for a while, but the more people do it the more everyone will end up paying the price.

When I was younger, I was occasionally pressured into unprotected sex, and I always felt bad afterwards. Sometimes it took months of testing to ensure I hadn't caught an STI. Eventually I decided it wasn't worth the anxiety. Having a hook up that leaves yourself or your partner feeling worried is NOT part of our grand plan.

Also, condoms can be unexpectedly useful. Some guys use rubbers to reduce sensitivity, which helps them delay their orgasm.

SAFER ORAL SEX

'Going down'—oral sex, blowjobs, eating pussy—is an STI risk. Wearing a condom or using a dental dam for oral sex is rare among hetero folks, although it's more common for sex workers (us escorts tend to have high safer sex standards). You may also encounter a partner who prefers barriers for oral if you're hanging out in the queer scene or with kinky folk. Some people use oral sex barriers because they've had an STI scare in the past.

Using a barrier for oral sex is A-OK. There are quite a few STIs that can be transmitted by giving or receiving head. Anyone who asks for safer oral sex should have their wishes respected. Remember, 'normal is bullshit'. Everyone has a right to feel safe.

THE SECOND LINE OF DEFENCE: STI TESTING

Using condoms is all well and good, but they aren't foolproof—they have a failure rate. Condoms don't prevent all STIs (see below). Also, some STIs don't show symptoms for a long time (or at all), so you could be infecting other people (and getting sicker by the day) and not realise. This can also mess with your fertility in the long term. If you're having sex (PIV or otherwise) it's important you get regular STI check-ups.

You can have an STI screen done by your doctor. Depending on where you live, you might be able to get a free check done at a local sexual health clinic. I like clinics because the doctors and nurses there are used to dealing with peoples' junk every day. Regular doctors aren't always perfectly sex-positive!

An STI screen involves a visual inspection and a blood test. You might also have swabs taken, which are basically oversized cotton wool buds that collect samples from your pussy, dick, throat, and/or ass to check for STIs. Having someone look at your bits can be confronting at first, but you get used to it. As a sex worker, I get tested every three months. It's so normal for me now that I usually end up having a conversation with my doctor about the weather.

Because some STIs don't show up straight away, one test isn't enough. You need to be tested regularly. My local sex therapist recommends testing every six months, or immediately if you notice a symptom such as discharge, sores, or anything out of the ordinary. Once a year is not enough, if you're a regular hook-up champion. Put a reminder in your diary and stick to it.

A CAUTIONARY NOTE ON HPV & HSV

There are STIs that condoms don't prevent—in particular, genital warts (Human Papilloma Virus, or HPV) and Herpes Simplex Virus (HSV). Both can be caught from people who don't show any symptoms. You can also catch herpes from someone if they go down on you when they have a cold sore (because the virus that causes cold sores is a similar type of virus to the one that causes herpes).

If you have HSV or HPV, see your doc to learn how to best prevent infecting others. If you spot any sores on people's junk, or on their lips, don't fuck them until a doctor has checked it out. Having HSV or HPV isn't a huge deal, it's super common. But the more persistent types of herpes infections can be a real nuisance unless you get medication. Also, genital warts put yourself (and your partners) at risk for cervical, anal, and throat cancer. If you see visible signs, get checked.

HYGIENE AND SAFETY (AKA, 'DON'T STICK THINGS WHERE THEY SHOULDN'T GO.')

Despite what porn suggests, it's a bad idea to stick things in your butt (or anyone's butt) and then in your pussy or mouth (or anyone's pussy/mouth). This results in infection or sickness. If you're into ass play, it's easy to get distracted and use the same fingers for a partner's pussy that you've just used for their ass. Bad idea—use a different hand, wash your hands, or use antibacterial wipes to ensure you're not transferring infection-causing germs. You can also use latex gloves for ass stuff (this is what the pros do, and gloves are easily obtained from your local supermarket).

Similarly, I recommend not appropriating household objects for your sex play. It might seem hot to get stuck into the veggie drawer or whatever, but shit goes wrong. A quick Google search will turn up many stories of people who got things stuck in their vaginas or asses that should never have gone there in the first place. You can read more about safer toy options in Part III of this book.

WHAT IF THERE'S A SAFER SEX ACCIDENT?

So, the condom broke. Or maybe it slipped. Or maybe you had a slip-up in judgement, and you didn't use barrier protection at all. (If the condom 'slipped' because someone took it off without your consent, that's sexual assault.) Safer sex accidents can also happen when we accidentally touch someone in a way that could spread STIs, or when we get our toys mixed up, or when cum lands somewhere unexpected. Any type of bodily fluid making contact with any orifice or sensitive area (such as your eyes) can be an STI risk.

An accident is stressful, especially if your safer sex standards are usually high. There's the risk of STIs and/or the risk of pregnancy, depending on your bits. It's normal for one (or both) of you to be freaking out. But before you completely lose your shit, get all the facts.

Some STIs are easy to catch, some are difficult. Luckily, the really tricky ones (HIV and hepatitis) are difficult to transmit. Your chance of catching them are low, unless you were engaging in a riskier sexual practice (such as anal sex or anything that involves blood-to-blood contact). Most common STIs are treated easily using medication.

SAFER SEX EMERGENCY ACTION

- **PEP treatment**—if you think you are at risk for HIV infection, you can access Post-Exposure Prophylaxis (PEP). This is a course of drugs that drastically lower your chances of becoming infected. But time is critical—the faster you get the treatment, the better it works. Most professionals recommend you start the drugs within 24 hours. So don't delay, get to your doctor or sexual health clinic straight away.

- **The 'morning-after' pill**—if there's a risk of pregnancy, a doctor can prescribe the morning-after pill, which is basically a big dose of synthetic hormones, like the oral contraceptive. This medication will lower the risk of you becoming pregnant. Like PEP, timing is everything. You need to take it within 24 hours for maximum effectiveness. Be aware, it can also make you throw up—I've had to take it twice, and both times I spewed on the way home from the chemist.

- **STI check-up**—if you go straight to your doctor, they can check you for STIs. This won't tell you if you've caught anything (because most of them take weeks to months to show up in tests). But it will be useful for your partner, because you'll be able to let them know of your status and give them some peace of mind. Your partner should also get checked and keep you informed. Your doctor can then advise you when to come back for a second test.

- **Stay safe for three months**—some STIs (such as HIV and hepatitis) can take up to three months to show up in tests. If you have other partners with whom you don't use barrier protection, such as long-term romantic partners, you need to do so until the window of opportunity has closed. Otherwise you could pass an STI to them, even though you don't show symptoms.

Having a condom break or catching an STI doesn't make you a bad person. It's one of those risks we try to control, but occasionally must deal with in order to be responsible. It's also important to remember that sometimes STIs don't show any symptoms at all, so if your partner does have something, they may not know. Don't take their word for it—get straight to the doctor.

TL;DR

- Consent is a human right—we all deserve to have our boundaries respected. It's also a tool for better sex; why guess when you can ask?
- If long conversations are too difficult, try using traffic light safe words. Green means go, orange means slow down/change direction, red means STOP.
- Sex 'on script' can be boring. Sex 'off script' encourages mindfulness, which in turn maximises your pleasure.
- Get skilled up on your safer sex; confidence is sexy.

So far, we've talked about connection, flirting, hot sexy play, safer sex... all the good stuff. Next, we need to talk about something a little less fun, but no less essential: how to get away afterwards without feeling awkward. This is what I call 'exit strategy.'

CHAPTER 8

EXIT STRATEGY

'I'm leaving,' he said.

It was seven a.m. on a Saturday. My one-night stand from the evening before was pulling his jeans on in my kitchen, while I was still sitting up in bed. His eyes were darting from side to side like an animal in a trap.

'Um, okay. Do you want a coffee?' I said. I didn't plan on getting his number, but I wasn't going to kick him out in a hurry.

He, on the other hand, seemed hell-bent on escape. "No thanks, I gotta go."

Later, I realised he hadn't even asked my address. I'd driven us home, so he had no idea where he was. This happened well before Uber or Google Maps. I sometimes wonder how he got home… did he stop and ask a stranger on the street for directions? Who knows?

I've lost count of the number of times someone has run out on me, gotten weird, ghosted me, or acted like an asshole, simply because they didn't know how to leave politely. Dating suffers from an epidemic of awkward exits.

We suck at ending relationships, even short-term ones. We're never sure if we're saying the right thing and we're often scared of hurting someone's feelings. And then there's the day-after shame: Did I do the wrong thing? Is it ok to sleep with someone but not want to date them?

This is why so much bad behaviour occurs after dates, when one partner (or both) tries to escape. We lack the communication skills, so we feel it's easier to ghost someone, run away, or act like a jerk, than to end things openly.

But if you're going to do hook ups the right way, you need to know how to leave without getting weird about it. As I pointed out in 'Why you Shouldn't Be an Asshole,' it's in our best interests to look after the people we're fucking. I believe that good hook ups are respectful, and respect means disentangling yourself gracefully after a sexual encounter.

This chapter will give you strategies for exit situations and some ideas for managing the post-hook-up blues. It's not always possible to make a perfect getaway, but you owe it to yourself, and to your partners, to try. Sex columnist Dan Savage has a 'campsite rule': leave your partners in a better state than you found them. It isn't a good hook up if your partner feels terrible afterwards, and you don't deserve to feel that way either. Off we go—here's how to exit, without feeling like a trapped animal.

Off we go—here's how to exit, without feeling like a trapped animal.

MAKING A GRACEFUL EXIT

There are three levels of exit difficulty: easy, moderate, and extreme. I have ways to deal with every situation, no matter how challenging.

THE EASY SCENARIO: A CLEAN GETAWAY

In this situation, everybody wants the same thing: to have fun, and to part ways.

The best way to make a clean getaway is to do your due diligence before you hook up. Being honest beforehand will avoid unpleasant surprises or hurt feelings. If you've advertised yourself as someone who's only looking for a hook up, and discussed this during the flirtation stage, then everyone understands. Once the hook up is done, you can say 'Thanks!' and move on.

I consider it polite to hang around after sex and talk for a while. This reassures my partner that I still respect them, and that I had a good time. Apart from that, you don't need to feel guilty for leaving, because it's exactly what you both negotiated.

USEFUL LINES

- 'Thanks, that was awesome. I'll be going now.'
- 'I had so much fun, but it's time for me to go. Want to do this again sometime?'
- 'See you round!'

THE MODERATE-DIFFICULTY SCENARIO: A CHANGE OF PLANS

Perhaps you were looking for a friend with benefits, but the sexual chemistry isn't right. Maybe you wanted a one-night stand, but halfway through you decide it's not fun anymore. Maybe something about the situation is off. Whatever the reason, it's totally okay to walk away.

You might feel guilty for killing the mood, but it's better to leave than to force yourself to stay in an uncomfortable situation. Be honest. People don't like rejection, but nobody can tell you that your feelings are wrong.

USEFUL LINES

- 'I'm sorry, this isn't working for me.'
- 'I'm sorry, I'm not feeling great about this. I've changed my mind.'
- 'I need to stop… something doesn't feel right.'

THE EXTREME SCENARIO: BATTLE OF WILLS

The Extreme Scenario is the one in which your partner is demanding something you don't want to give. It's best avoided by being totally honest with your partner when you first meet them, so that they're clear on your boundaries. But sometimes shit goes wrong anyway. People might have different expectations or change their minds. When this happens, whether it's malicious or misguided, it's not your fault.

Nobody should make you do anything you don't want. If your hook-up partner has expectations that aren't being met—whether it's sex, com-mitment, knowing your personal details, or anything else—you have no obligation to comply. If you go home with them but decide you don't want sex, you're allowed to leave. If you fuck them but don't want a relationship, you're allowed to say 'no.'

If you've been honest, you don't need to feel guilty about getting the hell outta there. Even if you haven't been honest, you still have the right to refuse anything you're not comfortable with.

USEFUL LINES

- 'I said I wasn't looking for a long-term relationship, and that hasn't changed. Sorry.'
- 'This isn't working for me, and I need to go now.'
- 'Like we agreed before, this was just sex. I like you, but that's just the way it is.'
- 'Sorry, I can't give you my number. It's against my rules.'
- 'That was fun, but you need to leave now.'

If one word is all you can muster, saying 'no' is your human right. Firmly stating your boundaries should be enough to make them back off. If it's not, the other person is an asshole and you should ditch them as quickly as possible.

Whenever our needs collide with the expectations of others, conflict follows. The whole process is worsened by the fact that most folks don't understand how to ask for consent or accept rejection. A good exit scenario is not about keeping everyone happy; it's about making sure everyone is being respected. Sometimes that involves brave words. Remember everything you've learned about radical honesty, because this is one of those times you really need it.

HOW TO DEAL WITH THE
DAY-AFTER BLUES

Did you know that sex messes with your brain? When we get close to others, our grey matter releases oxytocin. Known as the 'bonding hormone', it makes us feel loved and boosts our immune systems. When we experience pleasure from sex, our brains also get a shitload of dopamine and serotonin—the happy neurochemicals. This gives us a similar boost: we feel great, sometimes to the point of feeling 'high'—there's a reason we call love a drug!

Unfortunately, all these brain drugs must come from somewhere. We have a limited supply, a cache that usually only releases in small amounts, like having candy rationed out to you as a kid. When you have great sex, your brain blows most of its stocks at once, and the next day you might come up empty. Like overdoing it on lollies at Halloween, it leaves you with a sick feeling of 'what just happened?'

This phenomenon is called 'drop'. It's well known in the kink scene, where sex can go for hours and often involves big adrenaline highs. Afterwards, we sometimes find ourselves feeling flat, sad, empty, or just scatterbrained. Drop might happen right after sex, or it might kick in a day or two afterwards—everyone is different.

> **DROP:** The emotional crash that sometimes happens after an intensely enjoyable experience.

I'm guessing that drop is the reason some folks reckon casual sex is bad for you. The encounter feels good at the time, but a day or so later the sadness sets in. It seems like a confirmation of all those 'sex is bad' messages we get in bible class… but really, it's just a chemical imbalance in our heads.

Drop sucks. Getting past it requires support and self-care. The most important thing is being forewarned, so that if you wake depressed, you don't automatically assume the worst.

How can you avoid drop? You can't. Like a hangover after a night out drinking, an emotional hangover is something that must be weathered. How bad you feel will depend on your brain chemistry and your personality. There are some preventatives, mostly obvious stuff (like the ones prescribed for alcohol). Here are a few suggestions.

STRATEGIES TO PREVENT DROP

- Drink plenty of water
- Get a good nights' sleep
- Eat something healthy
- Physical activity (e.g. a walk or a gym workout)

Once the bad feelings have landed, it's important to take care of yourself until they pass. Below are my strategies for getting through.

HOW TO SURVIVE DROP

- **Know that it's brain chemistry, not reality**. My friend Rosie puts a reminder in her calendar before a date: 'Feel like shit today? It's only drop.'

- **Accept that the bad mood is here to stay**, at least for now. The quicker you accept it, the quicker it will pass.

- **Use your supports**. Friends are great for this. Call your mum and tell her you love her, if that helps. Whatever you do, contact the people in your life, to remind yourself that your recent conquest isn't the be-all and end-all. If you don't have friends and family available and you feel terrible, Lifeline (13 11 14) is a good go-to.

- **Use your self-care.** Stay home from work and watch movies, go for a run, lose yourself in a good book or listen to music. Give yourself permission to look after yourself, as if you were your own best friend.

- **Write your thoughts down.** I record my feelings about my sexual experiences in a notebook (an interesting read, I assure you). It helps me to get my head straight, re-live the good bits, and consider anything that doesn't feel right.

- **Don't make any major life decisions** while your brain chemistry is compromised. Your brain will be operating less efficiently for a couple of day,s as a result of its chemical meltdown. Don't quit your job or buy a kitten. You get the idea.

- **Tell shame to fuck off.** When we feel down, we often blame ourselves. We might also try to find reasons for why we feel shit: 'I suck at sex,' or, 'He hasn't called me,' or 'I'm a bad person.' You need to hold off on those thoughts. Think it over again once you feel better.

CELEBRATE, ASSESS, REPEAT

Any successful businessperson will tell you that the path to success is:

1. Celebrate what you just achieved.

2. Ask yourself, 'How can I be even better next time?'
3. Put those reflections into practice.

This is the advantage to dumping sex shame—rather than hiding from our experiences, we can learn from them. Instead of pretending it never happened, we can allow ourselves to feel good, while also asking 'How can I do even better?'

Corporations use this strategy to improve. It's how professionals become experts; they critique themselves and try again.

Just as I encourage you to debrief with your partner after sex, I also recommend you take some time alone to think about what just happened. Give yourself a mental high-five, if you want! But also ask yourself how you feel, what worked, and what didn't.

USEFUL QUESTIONS
- How are you feeling now?
- Did the hook up meet your needs?
- What did you do well?
- What do you need to improve on?
- What would you do differently next time?

My favourite question is, 'What did I enjoy the most?' It's nice to think over an experience, recall the best bits, and file them away on the trophy shelf of my brain.

The aftermath of a sexual encounter might leave you feeling down, lonely, or guilty. Sometimes it's drop, as described earlier. But it can also be helpful to explore any uncomfortable feelings to make sure you haven't been abused or disrespected (or abused/disrespected your partner). If bad feelings come up, talk with a close friend or a sex-positive therapist. Seek support and look after yourself.

TL;DR

- Most people suck at leaving after a hook up—it takes a while to learn how.
- Easy, hard, or demonic: no matter the difficulty, you still have the right to walk away.
- Feeling down a day or two after? It could be drop. Practice support and self-care until your brain has recovered.
- The best way to become an expert is to celebrate, self-debrief, then repeat the experiment.

Congratulations! You've reached a new level of sexual awareness. As you practice connecting, communicating, and perfecting your skills, you'll notice the difference.

Most folks think it's easier to just go along for the ride, but you know better: when we take responsibility for ourselves, we have more fun. Now you're ready to move to the next level as we enter Part III: your transformation into a hook-up champion.

PART III

FUCK THE WORLD BETTER

So, you've reached your destination… why not reach for the stars? Becoming a hook-up champion makes the world a better place.

I recently attended an escort booking for a husband-and-wife couple, visiting them at their apartment. I love introducing couples to threesomes—it's one of my favourite pastimes! But as soon as I walked through the door, I could sense their apprehension. The wife was sitting on the sofa with her knees pulled nearly to her ears and the husband was pacing the room, chewing on his fingernails.

'We've never done this before,' the wife admitted.

The clock was ticking—the couple had booked two hours of my (expensive) time, and that time was rapidly passing. If they'd been more experienced, I would have started flirting with them straight away. But it was obvious that this approach wasn't going to work. Instead, I sat with them on the couch and we had an honest conversation.

'This session is about both of you enjoying yourselves,' I said. 'We don't have to do anything you're not comfortable with. We don't have to have sex, or even get naked, if it doesn't feel right. Let's just take it slowly.'

Much later, we found ourselves lying side-by-side in their king-sized bed, limbs tangled, staring at the ceiling in post-orgasmic bliss.

'How was that for you?' I asked them.

'I was so nervous! But it was great.' the wife replied.

'Thanks,' said the husband, 'I would never have been able to try a threesome, if you hadn't made it feel so safe.'

Learning how to hook up gave me better sex. But there are other benefits—I'm able to look after my partners and ensure they have great experiences too. When we use our skills to improve the lives of others, we make the dating world safer and more enjoyable, which in turn makes it easier for everyone to get laid. This is what I call 'fucking the world better'—using our sexual superpowers for the benefit of all.

Lots of folks are hesitant to try new things because they've been treated badly in the past by their dates. They may have been shamed or had terrible sex. When bad stuff happens, those people are less likely to hook up in the future.

The antidote is you, my friend.

When we create a safe and respectful hook-up scene, more people are likely to give it a go. And that means more potential partners for you, me, and everyone else who knows their shit.

In Part III, I share the wealth of advanced knowledge I've accumulated during my years as an escort and hook-up enthusiast. You'll learn to survive sex disasters, flirt without being creepy, and guide your partners safely through the adventures that most folks only dream of—kink, threesomes, and much more. These skills will build on your knowledge and turn you into a warrior of the sexual universe.

The more you use this stuff to ensure your partners have great sex, the more things will improve for everyone. Hopefully, we'll end up surrounded by sex-positive adventurers who are down to fuck in the best possible way. That, friends, is my idea of utopia.

We're not there yet, but it needs to start somewhere—why not with you?

CHAPTER 9

WHEN DISASTER STRIKES

This chapter will help you handle yourself when things go wrong. As I've said before, sex is not without risk.

In my years as a sex worker, I've been stuck in some difficult situations. I've looked after drunk guys who were so nervous about hooking up with an escort that they downed an entire bottle of whisky before I arrived. I've counselled people through losing their virginity. I once hugged a crying woman in her kitchen, when she lost her cool in the middle of a threesome with her partner…

Awkward sex, brutal rejections, freak outs, uncooperative body parts… these occurrences might flatten a lesser adventurer. But not you! Even when things look bad, there's always something you can do about it. This chapter contains strategies for handling the drama that inevitably happens when hooking up. We'll examine what to do when the sex just isn't working, put some safeguards in place for dealing with distress, and build up your psychological resilience.

By anticipating the risks, you'll have strategies to deal with them. Hook-up champions, like boy scouts, are prepared for anything.

SURVIVING FREAK OUTS AND BREAKDOWNS

Ever had to comfort a crying woman in the middle of a sexual escapade? Here's another threesome story—one that's a little more dramatic!

A year or so ago, I had a couples' escort job booked in South Melbourne. My clients hadn't been together long but were very much in love… and they'd decided to try something new.

Things began well (drinks, canapes, flirting) and progressed well (bedroom, making out, getting naked.) But then everything fell apart. Halfway through the sexy stuff, the lady of the couple burst into tears and ran out of the bedroom.

She told us to keep going without her, which I didn't, of course (I'm not an asshole.) Instead, I we sat in her kitchen and I tried to find out what was wrong.

I discovered that the lady had some insecurities about the relationship. Seeing her partner with another woman caused those insecurities to feel overwhelming. None of us could have predicted it, least of all herself.

'It's just one of those things that happens,' I told her. 'Sometimes emotions come up, and it's okay.'

It really was.

Sex can be emotional in ways we don't expect. Sometimes the emotion is understandable—for example, getting mad at someone who's being an asshole, or feeling afraid because we're not safe. But upset can also happen for reasons that aren't immediately obvious.

COMMON EMOTIONAL SURPRISES

- **Jealousy**—of your partner, or perhaps something in the past that has nothing to do with the present situation.
- **Sadness**—did you know I sometimes burst into tears after orgasm? If I'm feeling sad in general, sex tends to make me emotional.
- **Insecurity or anxiety**—being naked and vulnerable in front of someone else can cause an insecure freak out, especially if you don't know your partner well.
- **Random laughing fits**—I don't even know if this counts as an emotion, but I'm going to list it anyway! As an escort, I once visited a client who had just dropped acid but had neglected to tell me. The only reason I figured it out was because he kept giggling while we were having sex. Aside from drug-induced states (which may or may not be your thing), having a laugh is great. Sex is supposed to be fun, not serious.
- **Anger or irritation**—Frustration and irritation are feelings we all have from time to time. But it's important to note that aggression that's directed at someone or used to threaten someone is NEVER okay.

What do we do when freak outs happen? Whether yourself, or your partner are doing the freaking, acknowledge what's happening. Stop, and name it.

USEFUL LINES

- 'Fuck, I just started feeling really sad all of a sudden.'
- 'I know this might be weird, but I was thinking about you and your last girlfriend, and now I feel really jealous.'
- 'Hey, you look upset, what's going on for you right now?'
- 'I feel kinda insecure at the moment. Can we stop for a sec?'
- 'Sorry you're not feeling great. Let's talk about it.'

Naming the emotion takes the sting out of it. If you can give yourself and your partner permission to be emotional, that will help you deal with it. Conversely, there's nothing worse than trying to pretend you're not upset. It's super awkward when you both know something is up, but nobody will talk about it.

Humans are weird, emotions are random, and that's okay. But there's another type of freak out that we need to talk about; one that can be overwhelming. If the emotion that comes up is linked to a previous traumatic event, that's called being 'triggered.'

WHAT'S AN EMOTIONAL TRIGGER?

An emotional trigger is anything in an encounter that causes you to remember a bad experience. If it's related to a traumatic experience—such as abuse, violence, or sexual assault—it's called a trauma trigger.

> **TRIGGER:** Anything that reminds you of a past event and causes an intense emotional reaction.

Maybe your date's deodorant is the same one your abusive ex used to wear. Maybe meeting at a place where you used to hang out with your dad makes you sad, because he's passed away. Maybe someone grabs you too roughly, and it reminds you of the time you were sexually assaulted. Triggers can happen innocently and sometimes they take us by surprise.

COMMON TRIGGERS

- Any sort of rough touch (particularly face slapping) if you've experienced domestic violence.
- Rape jokes (they remind people of all the times they've been raped—not fun).
- Grabbing the back of people's heads unexpectedly during oral sex (for the same reason as the previous point).

If you've been triggered, your number-one priority is your safety. Stop everything and get yourself to a safe place. Having support and self-care options ready beforehand is important if you know you're prone to having a trauma reaction.

If your hook-up partner has been triggered, it's your job to stop and care for them. Being triggered might mean freaking out, getting mad, or just shutting down. It's not always possible to tell when someone has been triggered, because they might not be able to speak or ask for help (this is why checking in during sex is so important). Once you do notice a problem, get them to a safe place and ask them what they need.

USEFUL LINES

- 'How are you feeling?'
- 'What can I do to help?'
- 'Let's stop and make sure you're okay.'

Water, blankets, or even some physical space might help - or might not, it just depends on the person. Do your best. You may not be able to make them feel better, but it's your job to look out for them.

I was a bit of an emo when I was twenty-four—you know, jet-black hair, facial piercings, all that stuff. One time, I picked up a girl at a metal gig and we went home together. But one we were in bed together, she froze up—legs crossed, eyes closed, not moving. I was confused, because she had asked to come home with me and I didn't know why her behaviour had changed so suddenly. I backed off, and we ended up having an awkward night lying side-by-side in bed, not touching

Looking back, it's obvious that she'd had some bad experiences in the past and was freaking out that night. She couldn't bring herself to speak about it—not surprising, considering we barely knew each other! Sadly, I was too shy to ask. I wish I'd been brave enough to say, 'Hey, I can see you're uncomfortable. What can I do to help you feel safer?'

Not all freak outs are manageable. If you're feeling out of your depth, call for help—Lifeline (13 11 14), or seek out partners, friends, or family for support.

THE ADVENTURE HANGOVER

Sometimes the best lessons in hook ups come from the times we fuck up, or the times we feel bad. These experiences are useful, if you pay attention rather than trying to block them out.

In Part II, we talked about 'drop'—the feelings of low mood that sometimes happen a day or two after a hook up. There's another, even more distressing, feeling that you might experience after a date—I call it the 'adventure hangover'.

I borrowed the term from a friend of mine. Here's the story: he picked up a girl online who was interested in having sex in public. It wasn't something he had done before, and he was nervous, but he decided to give it a go. They went to a local park and hooked up (I didn't get all the sexy details, but I'm pretty sure nobody was around at the time.)

Afterwards, my friend freaked out. Public sex was way out of his comfort zone. He'd pushed himself to do it anyway, but all that adventuring resulted in a backlash of shame and depression.

Sometimes when we go on a sexual adventure, we journey further out of our comfort zones than we're ready for. Then we feel scared and inadequate, and we wonder if we did the wrong thing. This is the basis of the 'adventure hangover.'

ADVENTURE HANGOVER:
An emotional backlash after stepping too far out of your comfort zone.

Feeling this way doesn't mean you're a bad person. It just means you went further or faster than you were ready to go at that time. Keep in mind that 'going too far' means different things to different people. For some folks, it might mean getting into some kink play or going to a sex party. For others, just having a one-night stand is challenging. My mate Rosie describes it thus: 'Leaving your comfort zone is like a rubber band—the further you stretch, the worse the snap-back.'

Adventure hangovers are difficult to avoid because we don't always know how much adventure is too much. The best advice I can offer is this: listen to your fear before you do something wild and consider whether you need to slow down. Fear is your warning light. Use it, don't ignore it.

Over-stretching yourself isn't the end of the world—in fact, you've learned something important. Sometimes we don't know where our limits are until we step on them, even if stepping on them feels like shit. And you never know—something that's too scary one day, might be okay the next. Don't be afraid to try again as you get used to the idea and see if your feelings have changed.

WHEN IT'S JUST NOT WORKING

Being human can really suck. Leg cramps, jiggly bits, weird orgasm faces… why can't sex be perfect, like in the movies? The fact is, our bodies are awkward and imperfect, and the sex we have follows suit. There's no guarantee of a perfect 10/10 hook up—but hey, the uncertainty is what makes it fun, right?

Sometimes, despite all your best efforts, the sex just doesn't work out the way you planned. My lesson in this came in 2013, when I hooked up with a friend of mine after a bush doof (that's Aussie slang for 'electronic music festival in the forest.') He was a hippie raver, and we'd been flirting for years.

I assumed our hook up would be amazing, because we were so keen on each other. And you know what they say about assumptions, right?

The sex just… didn't work. It took me by surprise, because emotional connection and sexual attraction usually lead to a great sexual experience. But not this time! Even though we were both making an effort, it didn't feel right.

What did I do? I shrugged and wrote the experience off as a failed experiment. We stayed friends, but I never tried to shag him again.

Remember the bullshit we talked about in Part I? There's a lot of cultural pressure to be perfect in bed, and we often feel ashamed of ourselves if things don't turn out exactly the way we want. But sex is supposed to be unpredictable, awkward, and imperfect. Maybe it's time to cut yourself some slack. Otherwise every time the sex isn't great, you're going to feel as though it's all your fault. Nobody deserves that kind of pressure.

Here are a few ways a hook up can go awry.

RUNNING OUT OF STEAM

Sex requires a lot of energy, especially if you're partial to the headboard-banging, two-hour-marathon variety. We don't always have the stamina for this stuff. How crazy you can get in the bedroom depends on your level of physical fitness, how much sleep you've had, your stress levels, and whether you just completed leg day at the gym. If you're struggling, there's no shame in stopping, slowing down, taking a break or asking your partner to take over for a while.

Just as we aren't born knowing how to do sex, we also aren't born with the necessary physical capabilities. You need very particular muscles to get it on, and the only way you develop them is through practice. Find the moves that work for your body and change up the script when necessary to give yourself a rest.

NOT GETTING HARD OR NOT GETTING WET

Bodies don't always cooperate. It's assumed that if someone is turned on, they'll get hard or get wet (or some combination of the two) and stay that way for the entire duration of the sexual experience.

News flash: most peoples' bodies don't work this way.

Most people take a while to get hard or wet, and some people don't self-lubricate at all. Also, arousal is closely linked to emotional state. Any sort of anxiety makes things difficult. I see it all the time in my work, where guys who I've just met invariably have trouble getting it up, because they're so nervous.

Big Pharma would have you believe that sexual issues with penises and vaginas are a medical problem. Some are, but mostly it's just the way individual bodies work. Our crappy macho culture insists that a guy who can't get a hard on is less of a man, and that a woman who doesn't get wet isn't turned on. That's bullshit. Our bodies are never entirely under our control.

If your bits aren't performing as expected, getting relaxed and giving yourself a break is the first line of defence. The second is a good lubricant. The third is having some amazing sex moves that don't involve penetration, so that you can take the pressure off. Isn't it lucky you read Part II?

NOT GETTING TO ORGASM

Did you know that both guys and girls sometimes have trouble cumming when they're nervous? I've met more than one person who couldn't get hard until they were relaxed, and some who couldn't cum until they were comfortable around me. This is just how bodies work—they're sensitive to our emotional states.

If you're okay with it, you may be able to get yourself off using your hand or a toy and let the other person watch. Or you could enjoy the sex and save the orgasm for later, when you're alone. Sex can be great whether you cum or not. That's what going off script is all about.

Penis owners sometimes experience 'death grip syndrome'—when a guy is so used to masturbating in a particular way that nothing else, including regular sex, gets him to orgasm. The cure for this is to stop masturbating for a while until the habit fades. Failing that, I recommend talking with a sex therapist.

A lot of hetero guys judge their sexual performance by how many orgasms they give their female partner. This is a generous attitude, but it's useful to keep in mind that some vagina-owners have difficulties cumming with new partners, or at all. I'm one of these people—I don't usually cum during partnered sex, I either use my toy collection or wait until later. If I feel pressured, it takes the fun out of the whole encounter.

Your hook-up partner may or may not be forthcoming about the best way to get them off, depending on their level of confidence. You're probably going to have to ask (I bet this advice is starting to sound familiar!) If they don't want to cum, or aren't able to, it's better to respect their preferences than treat the situation like some sort of personal challenge.

Sex isn't a race to the finish line. Orgasms are great, but it's more important to go with the flow. If having trouble cumming bothers you, visiting a sex therapist is a great idea. But it's not always a problem to be fixed; everyone's bodies work differently.

HAVING SEX HURTS

Sex should not hurt (well, unless you're kinky and you've asked someone to flagellate you). What I mean is, sexual intercourse should not hurt, ever. If it hurts, stop and work out what's going wrong. Usually it's just a matter of not using enough lube. Sometimes the angle needs adjusting, or the position isn't right for you. Sometimes there's a size mismatch—a large cock and a small pussy or anxious butt hole—and you need to slow down and relax. But persistent pain is a problem that needs to be checked out by a doctor.

If you're a vagina-owning person, it could be an STI or urinary tract infection. There's also a condition called vaginismus, which causes the muscles of the vag to seize up during sex. It's incredibly painful, and it doesn't go away on its own—you need to see a specialist. Some physiotherapists also treat vaginismus (usually those who work in reproductive health.)

In a worst-case scenario, severe, ongoing pain could also be a sign of endometriosis or cancer. Don't hesitate—get it checked out! Don't put up with painful sex.

IT JUST DOESN'T FEEL RIGHT

As I mentioned earlier, sometimes the chemistry just isn't there. When I meet someone new, I can usually tell whether we're sexually compatible. If our connection is good, if I like them, if they kiss well, then I can be pretty sure we're going to get along. But sometimes it doesn't turn out that way. Sometimes sex is awkward, and I spend most of the time thinking 'why am I here?' instead of concentrating on what I'm doing.

Sometimes people just don't click when they hook up. It's nobody's fault and there's no shame in it, but you do need to notice and stop having sex with them.

There's often this assumption that, once we start fucking someone, we have to see it through to the end. That's the script—sex isn't over until the guy cums. Sometimes it's less like a script and more like being on a ride you can't get off! But if it's not fun, there's no point continuing. You're only forcing yourself (and everyone else) to have a bad time.

USEFUL LINES
- 'Hey, can we take a break? I'm not feeling it right now.'
- 'Sorry, this isn't working for me.'

Speaking up about mediocre sex is challenging. Folks tend to take it personally because the script tells us that stopping halfway means we've failed. Tell your hook up the truth: sometimes it just doesn't work. It's not a failure to halt bad sex. You're doing everyone a favour.

Still not sure? Here's something else to consider: putting up with bad sex does more harm than just ruin the mood. When you ignore your feelings, you're training your brain to associate sex with obligation, rather than pleasure. Do it too often, and you might forget how to enjoy yourself.

HOW TO SURVIVE REJECTION

Hearing 'no' is difficult, especially when it's coming from a potential sexual partner.

Recently, someone at a kink party turned me down. I'd met him before, and we both got along well. After we'd chatted for a while, I asked him if he wanted to play. His reply was a flat, 'No thanks'.

For me, the rejection is a whole-body feeling, and this time was no different. It started at the top of my head and worked its way down. My face turned red, and the back of my neck tensed. My mouth went dry, my heart hurt, and my stomach churned. I felt an embarrassment that boiled all the way to my toes.

Then the thoughts came: Why would he say no to me? Had I done something wrong? Was there something wrong with me? Was it wrong to even ask in the first place? Completely unaware of my mental turmoil, the guy in question wandered off and started making out with my best friend. I stood and watched them as I processed my uncomfortable feelings.

Rejection is an inevitable part of the hook up experience. To find the right person, you have to meet lots of folks that aren't right. And nobody is a mind-reader in the bedroom, so you'll hear, 'No, thanks,' from time to time.

Yet for some reason, every time we hear 'no,' it feels personal. Rejection taps into all our deepest fears—it's an arrow pointing straight at the stuff we dislike about ourselves. Whatever your insecurities, rejection has a way of bringing the worst of these to the surface of your psyche.

REASONS REJECTION HURTS

- **It echoes past experiences** of being told we're not good enough.
- **It reminds us of our own insecurity**—we feel as though we've been found out.
- **It feels like failure**, because society tells us we should know what we're doing when it comes to sex.
- **It triggers our feelings of shame** around sex.

Thing is, that 'no' is usually more about the other person than it is about you. Rejection isn't failure; it's a sign something isn't working. Perhaps you aren't their type, or they're having a bad day. Perhaps there's some little thing (or a big thing) that means you're incompatible. Perhaps they do like you, but they don't like the specific type of play you've suggested. Not everyone is designed to fit together and dating success doesn't mean fucking every person you meet. As we've established, success is all about finding the right people and doing the things that you both enjoy.

Rejection performs an essential function, whether you're doing the rejecting or receiving it. It makes the situation clear and frees us up to work out our next move. Furthermore, your potential partner is treating you with respect by being honest, instead of leading you on. When it happens to me, I take some deep breaths, remind myself of this, and wait for the bad feelings to pass. Sometimes that takes a while. In the meantime, I demonstrate appreciation for my partner's honesty by saying, 'thank you.'

USEFUL LINES

- 'Thanks for being so up front.'
- 'Okay, I hear you.'
- 'I appreciate you being honest.'
- 'Thanks, I respect that.'

Rejection performs an essential function, whether you're doing the rejecting or receiving it. It makes the situation clear and frees us up to work out our next move. Furthermore, your potential partner is treating you with respect by being honest. When it happens to me, I take some deep breaths and wait for the bad feelings to pass (sometimes that takes a while). In the meantime, I demonstrate appreciation for my partner's honesty by saying, 'thank you.'

Becoming practised at hearing a 'no' is the best kind of emotional bullet-proofing. The better you can handle a 'no', the less threatening rejection becomes—and the more likely someone is to trust you in the future.

CONSENT VIOLATION AND SEXUAL ASSAULT

Remember what it was like being a kid? When you couldn't reach cupboard doors, and adults were towering creatures that were always saying 'no'? Maybe your childhood was happy, or maybe it wasn't. Regardless, we've all experienced feeling small and powerless.

I wasn't an unhappy child, but I loved becoming an adult because it meant that nobody could tell me what to do any more. I was in charge of where I went and who I hung out with… well, mostly. If you've ever had an asshole boss, you'll know that being an adult can be hard too.

Remember the boundaries diagram we looked at in Chapter Seven? Our personal boundaries include our immediate physical space, our thoughts, and our feelings. Our boundaries are our business—and when others try to tell us what to do, it can feel really fucking awful.

I used to have a mate called Dave who had another mate called Johnno. Dave was a friendly guy who loved card games. Johnno was… well, not so great. The night we first met, he'd been drinking all afternoon, and he wanted me to sit in his lap. I was only nineteen at the time and I wasn't keen on that, thanks very much! But he kept hassling me, and I had no idea how to say 'no' without pissing him off. So, I perched uncomfortably on his knee for the whole night. (He had bony knees, FYI.)

I felt terrible. It wasn't just the unwanted physical touch. I felt powerless—he could make me do things I didn't want to, and he didn't seem to care if I was uncomfortable. I was so scared of offending him that I couldn't have spoken up even if I knew the words to say. What if he decided he wanted to kiss me? What if he told me to have sex with him? I wouldn't have been able to say no.

This is the tricky thing about consent violation: sometimes it happens because your partner is an asshole who doesn't care about your feelings. Sometimes it's because they assume you want what they want, and it never occurs to them to ask. Sometimes they don't know how to ask, so they just go for it and hope for the best.

And sometimes it's a little of everything. Because we're not sure how to ask, or caring seems too hard, it's easier to pretend everything is okay and ignore the distress signals.

I know this, because I've done it too.

MY STORY: BEING A PERPETRATOR OF SEXUAL VIOLENCE

Twelve years ago, I went on a holiday to New Zealand with a bunch of friends. They were single, sexy, hard-partying folk. One night, a female friend and I went bar-hopping in search of a hook up.

It was a Monday, so the pubs were mostly empty. But we did meet one dude who was having a few beers after work. He was about twenty years old. We started drinking with him, and after a while we invited him back to our hotel for a threesome. He declined because he already had a girlfriend.

Undeterred, we kept drinking with him. We figured he might change his mind, and as we had few other options, we considered him our last hope of getting laid. He ended up getting pretty wasted. We were drunk too, but not nearly as much.

We convinced him to come back to our hotel room 'just for a drink'. Then we started making out with him—he was extremely drunk by now, and his phone kept ringing because his girlfriend was worried about him.

Eventually we ended up naked with him.

I'm pretty sure it was his first three-way. Every guy wants to have a three-some, right? But he never stopped looking worried. Halfway through the sex, he jumped up from the bed, pulled his pants on, apologised and ran out of the room.

The next day I felt terrible. I thought it was just the hangover. But as I walked down the street at seven in the morning to get myself a coffee, our partner from the night before was standing on the footpath, waiting to cross the road. When he saw me, he hung his head and turned away. And in that moment, I realised that I'd done something terribly wrong.

I didn't understand what had happened until years later, after I learned more about consent. At the time I thought it was just bad sex, but in time I came to understand differently. It wasn't just a wild night—it was sexual assault.

He had said 'no' my friend and I in the bar—ignoring him was our first failure. Then we'd invited him back to our room under false pretences ('it's just for a drink') and started getting sexy without asking him. He was drunk, and much younger than us—we were assertive and much more experienced. Lastly, we didn't pay attention to his uncomfortable body language. When I recall that night, it's clear that he was struggling to get out of the situation.

It seems so obvious now. How did I miss the signs?

At the time, I lacked knowledge and self-awareness. I tended to see men as sexual predators and women as sexual victims. I didn't realise it was possible to pressure a guy into doing something he didn't want—I was completely unaware of my own power. I also didn't consider that he might have trouble saying 'no.' Guys often feel as though they can't refuse sex for fear of looking un-manly; can you imagine what his male friends would have said, if he told them he'd turned down a ménage à trois?

I was also being an asshole. When we set out that night, we were looking for a conquest, not a person. I was focused on what he could give me, not on what he wanted. Because I didn't spend time connecting with him, I missed his distress signals.

I don't know his name or number, so I can't apologise. I often wonder what effect that night had on him; did his girlfriend break up with him? Did he stop trusting strangers? Did he blame himself? I'll never know. Whether the harm we did was minor or devastating, I'll never be able to undo it. It's something I'll always be ashamed of.

Realising that I was capable of hurting others caused me to change how I do things. When I ask someone for their number, ask them on a date, or ask them for sex, I'm now consider their needs too. I pay attention to body language and check in if my partner looks hesitant. I make it clear that a 'no' is welcome—and if I hear one, I take it seriously.

Think you could never violate someone's consent? I thought the same. None of my efforts to do better will ever erase the shame I feel for hurting someone else. Please learn from my mistake, so you don't have to learn from your own... it's a regret you'd be better off without.

WHAT TO DO IF YOU'RE SEXUALLY ASSAULTED

Consent violation happens often, to people of all genders. Sometimes, it's due to ignorance. Sometimes, carelessness. Sometimes it's because our partner turns out to be an asshole who doesn't care about our wellbeing.

You can't always tell whether a person is trustworthy. Sometimes it happens even when we do all we can to keep ourselves safe.

If you're sexually assaulted, don't just rely on my advice. Seek out whatever form of help is right for you. This is heavy stuff and, as always, you are the ultimate expert in yourself.

If you're injured or in danger, please call emergency services immediately (000 in Australia). If you're at risk of self-harm or are in crisis, I recommend Lifeline (13 11 14).

ReachOut Australia defines sexual assault as 'any unwanted sexual behaviour that makes a person feel uncomfortable, threatened or scared.'

This includes:

- **Rape**: forced, unwanted sex or sexual acts.
- **Child sexual abuse**: using power over a child to involve that child in sexual activity.
- **Indecent assault**: indecent behaviour before, during or after an assault.

Sexual assault includes any unwanted sexual contact, not just penetration. It can happen to any gender.

> **SEXUAL ASSAULT:** Any unwanted sexual contact or behaviour.

If this has happened to you, please know that it is not your fault. You have a right to be safe and to be taken seriously when you seek help. Here is the advice CASA (the Centre Against Sexual Assault) gives if you have been sexually assaulted:

'You have the option to report the crime to police. You don't have an obligation to report, and you may also be able to report and request that no further action is taken. It's recommended that you report as soon as possible after the incident, because the sooner you speak to the police the easier it is for them to get the evidence they will need, should you proceed with charges. But there is no time limit on reporting a sexual assault to police. No matter how long you wait, you still have the right to report.'

Unless you're in immediate danger, I recommend calling a sexual assault helpline such as 1800 RESPECT or CASA for advice before speaking with police. You don't know who you'll end up talking to at the cop shop, and how well you're treated just depends on the person (sorry cops, some of you need to lift your game). In addition to providing support, a sexual assault service can brief you on the legal process and advise on preserving evidence. If you don't have access to a specialist organisation, a trusted friend or family member is also a good support.

EMERGENCY CONTACTS (AUSTRALIA)
- Sexual Assault Crisis Line: 1800 806 292
- 1800 RESPECT: 1800 737 732
- Lifeline: 13 11 14

'WHAT IF I'M THE PERPETRATOR?'

Learning about consent can be an uncomfortable experience—it makes us aware of how casually we have violated the boundaries of our partners in the past. Sometimes they are small mistakes and we resolve to do better. But sometimes we realise that we've fucked up badly—hurt, traumatised, or sexually assaulted someone.

If this is you, you're probably going to feel bad about it. But feeling bad isn't what helps. You need to take responsibility.

Taking responsibility means owning up to your behaviour and doing your best to make amends. How might you be able to address the problem? If you have permission to contact the person you've assaulted, ask them what they need from you. Listen to them and acknowledge the hurt you've caused. Then ask yourself—what went wrong? What can you do to be better in the future?

Dealing with being a perpetrator of sexual assault isn't as easy as erasing something off a whiteboard; you don't get to pretend it never happened. But there's something useful that does happen—the kind of personal growth you can't experience any other way. You have the power to act like a good human being.

A good person isn't someone who never fucks up; it's someone who takes responsibility for their actions. Taking responsibility means living with the consequences. You might lose a partner, feel guilty, alienate friends, or face disciplinary action. Whatever happens, square up to it. It's the only way we get better.

TL;DR

- Freak outs and emotional upsets happen—it's not the end of the world, but you do need to acknowledge it, otherwise the situation gets totes awkward.
- Sometimes sex doesn't work exactly the way we hoped. Bodies aren't perfect, and sometimes we just don't connect.
- Rejection is a fearsome beast, but it gets easier with practice. Rejection resilience is crucial—if you're too scared to hear 'no', you're never going to be able to ask.
- Consent violation sucks, especially if you're the victim. Make sure you're safe and seek support.
- … and it also sucks for the perpetrator—you don't want that stuff on your conscience! If you're responsible, resolve to do better. We all deserve to have our boundaries respected.

For the committed sexual adventurer, the occasional challenge is inevitable. It's not easy but being forewarned really helps.

Our next chapter will build on your social skills to allow you to visit some very interesting places… from learning how to say 'no' to managing an open relationship, I'll lay out the social skills you need for the advanced sex adventures that are coming your way.

CHAPTER 10

ADVANCED SOCIAL SKILLS

I feel as though you know me quite well by now, so I'm going to let you in on a secret: I'm still socially awkward as fuck.

I'm an introvert, which means I stand in the kitchen at parties and mix drinks to avoid speaking to people. I'm naturally shy, so unless you ask me a direct question about myself, I'll happily weld my lips shut and spend hours listening to you talk about your problems. Lastly, I'm a bit of a weirdo. I've never felt like I fit in, no matter how much my friends assure me to the contrary. This feeling of alienation makes it difficult to strike up conversations, start friendships, and snag sexual partners.

So how did I get past this stuff to become confident at hook ups? Practice.

Sometimes we get hung up on the ways we think we're not good enough. We tell ourselves that we're not good at parties or no good at talking to girls. And then those stories become so habitual that we forget one simple fact: we are capable of change. All it takes is a willingness to try doing things differently.

This chapter shows you how to navigate complex social situations in search of better hook ups. We start by mastering the word 'no,' so you can stand up for yourself with confidence. Then I'll show you how to flirt without invading someone's personal space. Finally, we bring up the dreaded 'R' word... Relationship. Whether you're considering opening your relationship or looking for an ongoing affair, I have some ideas to get you started.

HOW TO SAY 'NO' WITH CONFIDENCE

Being able to say 'no' is just as important as being able to hear it.

Other folks aren't mind-readers. We like to think that everyone can pick up on our social cues, but honestly, it's difficult—this is why sitcoms never run out of material. The only way to be sure that your date knows where you stand is to communicate with them.

Because so much of our social interaction is nonverbal and indirect, saying 'no' often feels rude. We may worry about being ridiculed or shamed. If someone has a bad reaction to a 'no', we blame ourselves. However, when you tell someone 'Sorry, I'm not interested,' or 'Sorry, I don't want to do that,' you're doing them a favour. They probably aren't aware of your feelings; you're giving them the information they need. Saying 'no' is a compassionate act that helps everyone.

USEFUL LINES
- 'Thanks, but no thanks.'

- 'I appreciate the offer, but I'm not up for that.'
- 'Thanks for asking, but I'm going to say no.'
- 'Sorry, I'm not into that.'

When you say 'no,' remember that the other person's reaction is not your responsibility. You might feel guilty if you reject someone and they take it badly. But your rights are more important than their hurt feelings.

WHEN 'NO' DOESN'T WORK

What if your 'no' isn't respected? It's awful when you decline a date or sexual activity and the other person keeps pressuring you—or, worse, they just go ahead and do it anyway. Being harassed or sexually assaulted can be devastating—sometimes so devastating that we avoid saying 'no' simply because we're afraid of realising that we're being abused.

Other times, you might feel like you're in danger, and that resisting will escalate the situation. This is one way sexual assault can happen—we're worried that our partner will hurt us so we shut up and hope to get through it. If you don't feel safe saying 'no,' please use your own judgement. Your safety is important.

Unfortunately, a 'no' won't stop someone who intends to hurt you. But there's an advantage to saying it at least once: you'll find out whether that person is an asshole. If you haven't tried to say 'no,' it may be unclear whether you're really in danger. But if you state your boundaries and those boundaries are ignored, then you'll know it's time to get the hell outta there.

In short: a 'no' will help a good person understand what you need. And it will help you identify an asshole, so you can get as far away from them as possible.

Do you feel awkward saying 'no?' Here's a useful game I learned at a workshop. It's great to play with regular partners, or even friends, to get used to asserting your boundaries.

HOW TO PLAY THE 'NO' GAME

Player 1: Asks Player 2 for something, e.g., 'Can I buy you a drink?'

Player 2: 'Thanks, but no thanks.'

Then, you swap over...

Player 2: Asks Player 1 for something, e.g., 'Can I touch your butt?'

Player 1: 'Thanks, but no thanks.'

Keep swapping roles, asking and refusing for as long as it takes to get used to saying 'no'.

This game can feel a bit weird at first, like learning a new language. I like to start with ridiculous requests, because it makes the game non-threatening: 'Can I take your beer and throw it at the bartender?' As you start to feel comfortable, try more realistic requests such as, 'Can I take your pants off?' Practising in a safe environment makes a huge difference when the time comes to say 'no' in a real-life situation.

One of the best things about learning to say 'no' is that it becomes easier to say 'yes'. When I was younger, I was scared to try new things because I was worried that I wouldn't be able to stop if I wanted to. This meant that I missed out on a lot of sexy adventures. Now that I'm more practised, I have lots of fun—threesomes, kink, hook-up escapades—that would have been way out of my comfort zone a few years ago. I feel brave enough to experiment, because I know I can speak up if I change my mind.

IS IT FLIRTING OR HARASSMENT? A QUICK-N-DIRTY GUIDE

It's not illegal to talk to someone you don't know. If we never spoke to strangers, we'd never make new friends. And before apps and dating sites came along, there was only one way to find new sexual partners, which was to approach them in person. Even in this digital age, talking to someone you've just met is still a valid way to connect. But it's amazing how often flirting can become outright sexual harassment. Before chatting someone up, you need to be clear on the difference.

Before you ask: this advice is for everyone, not just men. But it's true that guys are often the culprits. As I write this, I'm sitting in a pub with a female friend. A bloke just came over to us and asked if we had a lighter. Neither of us smoke, so we said no. Five minutes later, he's back at our table, wanting to know where the good clubs are. It's five p.m. on a Wednesday, mate! Clearly, he's hoping to strike up a friendship with one or both of us—probably my friend, who she smiled at him when we sat down. But we have our notebooks and laptops out, and it should be obvious that we're working and not looking for dates.

He's not a bad guy. He's just having a go at chatting to girls in a bar, though perhaps with less social awareness than average. But despite our polite disinterest, he keeps coming back. We don't want to say 'fuck off' because we can see he doesn't mean any harm. Also, he's had a few drinks and we're afraid that telling him to go away might make him angry. So, like many women do, we just sit here, trying not to make eye contact and hoping that he gets the hint.

Experiences like this are why it can be so difficult to talk to women in public—even when we do want to meet people, we'll often avoid conversation with strangers because we're scared of awkwardness and confrontation.

But it's not just guys who are the problem. Most people suck at flirting—I know I've been sexually inappropriate and insensitive at times. I've often succumbed to 'dickful thinking'—a tendency to assume someone else is interested, just because we're hot for them. I may not have a dick, but I've missed plenty of nonverbal 'fuck off' signals!

I've also been the victim of sexual harassment by other women. Because our gendered culture assumes women are never the sexual aggressors, some ladies aren't aware of the personal space of others.

When I was twenty, I used to hang out at a lesbian bar in Sydney with my friends. The older ladies all had punk haircuts and acted tough. I thought they were cool. But one time, a woman took a liking to me and got all up in my face about it. She told me I was a 'keeper', and then literally picked me up and started carrying me away from the pub, down the street. I mean, what the fuck? I was saying 'put me down' but she laughed it off. To be clear, this was someone I had never met, and we had NOT agreed to any physical contact. I didn't know where she was taking me. Finally, I convinced her to put me down on the sidewalk and I ran back to my friends.

I don't think she wanted to abduct me; she was simply demonstrating that she was bigger, stronger, and tougher than me. Because she found me attractive, she thought she could do whatever she wanted. And it sucked. Being sexually harassed feels like shit, no matter who does it.

Let's consider the problem from every angle—how to avoid harassing others and how to disentangle yourself when someone invades your personal space.

I have two strategies for hitting on people without sexually harassing them:

1. THE ROCK TEST

The 'Rock Test' was created by Anne Victoria Clark, in a blog post for Medium. You can find the link in the Further Reading section at the end if this book (and I highly recommend it). The piece is sarcastic, but it does function as a practical technique. Here's the basic idea.

Dwayne 'The Rock' Johnson is a fine actor and all-round human being. He's also built like a tank and could probably tear you limb-from-limb. If you saw The Rock in the street, would you walk up to him and say, 'Hey babe, want some dick?' Would you come up behind him and grab his butt? Would you shove yourself into the middle of a conversation he was having with friends? Not unless you had a death wish.

So, what would be appropriate? Something like, 'Hey, just wanted to say I think you're awesome!' or perhaps 'Do you mind if I interrupt to say hi?' This is how it works: would you say it to The Rock, or would you keep it to yourself in case he beat your head in? If you answered the latter, don't say it to a hottie at your local drinking establishment.

2. GIVE THEM SPACE TO SAY 'NO'

Pickup artists (PUAs) use a variation on this—they call it the 'time constraint.' They'll walk up to a woman and say, 'Hi! I have to go and meet my friends over there in one minute, but I'd love to speak with you first.' The time limit makes women more open to listening, because they feel safer—they know he will move on in a moment. This gives the PUA the time he needs to work his magic (by which I mean, bullshit).

The bit these guys are doing wrong is failing to go away. Have you heard the phrase 'if you love something, set it free'? Here's the right way to do it: say hi, state your time limit ('I'm going back to my table in a second, but I just wanted to let you know that…') and your invitation ('… I think you look interesting and I'd love to chat with you') then walk away.

USEFUL LINES

- 'Hi! I'm just passing by, but I wanted to say I'd love to talk with you – let me know if you're interested.'
- 'Hi! You seem awesome. I'll be right over there if you want to buy me a drink.'

Giving someone space is a good strategy—it shows you're not desperate and gives them time to think about whether or not they want to engage with you. If they do decide to come over and talk, you'll know the exchange is genuine and not just for fear of offending you.

To pull off this move you need to be comfortable with rejection. You're giving your partner an 'easy out' by walking away. Giving the other person space to say 'no' demonstrates respect, which is an attractive characteristic in a potential hook up. But you must be genuine. If they don't respond to your offer, leave them alone.

'WHAT IF I'M THE TARGET?'

I don't want to offer too much advice on how to avoid harassment, because I don't think it's the victim's job to stop it from happening. Ideally, the person doing the harassing should learn to do better. However, if you find yourself in a situation where this isn't happening, here are a few ideas that might help.

1. **Safety first.** Whatever you do, don't take action if you think your safety is at risk. Sometimes we find ourselves in situations that are impossible to escape from unscathed. There might be the threat of violence, you might be in an isolated location… or the person harassing you might be your boss, and you're worried about losing your job. If this has happened to you, I'm sorry. It's not your fault. Please use your own judgement to decide what's best for you.

2. **Gather your allies.** My friends and I used to have a secret code—if someone tried to hit on one of us at a club and we weren't interested, we'd introduce ourselves to the unsuspecting guy as 'Martha'. This was a signal that we wanted to be rescued, and our friends would immediately make up some sort of excuse to get us off the dance floor. I'm told the Queen does something similar at public events: using the position of her handbag on her arm to signal her security staff. If you have allies, use them.

3. **Say 'no'.** Say it confidently, respectfully and in a tone that de-escalates the situation. Security guards are good at this—they project confidence, in a low-key manner. Good humour can be useful—similarly to the way guys rib each other: 'Haha, sorry, no, see ya later!' A 'no' delivered with confidence and good humour is more effective than a scared or angry 'no' that increases the tension. Of course, there's no guarantee that saying it the 'right way' is going to work, which brings me to the next point…

4. **The other person's reaction is not your responsibility.** As we discussed earlier in the chapter, you can't control how people will react to rejection. You can only do your best and walk away if they act like assholes. You always have a right to say 'no.'

A NOTE ON DICK PICS (AND SEXTING IN GENERAL)

Harassment isn't just about physical space. It's also about mental space and the space in front of our eyeballs. Folks have the same rights online as they do in public—that is, the right to have their boundaries respected, and to be free of assault and abuse. Sending an unasked-for photo of your genitals is the equivalent of running up to someone on the street and pulling down your pants: it's a sexual violation.

Sexting (sending someone sexually explicit text, photos or video) can be fun, but it must be consensual. Some people feel that whenever an online interaction gets sexy, permission is automatically being granted for the sending of naked pics. But unless you have clear consent, showing someone your genitals is indecent assault. There's nothing wrong with photos of your junk, and some folks love it. But naked pics aren't okay unless the person says, 'Yes, please sext me!'

I've had many a potential date spoiled because, in the middle of a conversation about their job or pets or whatever, they suddenly decided to send me a dick pic. My reply is usually thus: 'Why did you have to go and ruin everything?' If someone doesn't respect my consent via text message, I don't trust them to respect me in person.

If you're interested in the art of sexting, Tina Horn has written a great book called *Sexting: The Grownup's Little Book of Sex Tips for Getting Dirty Digitally*. It goes into the dos and don'ts in more detail, and also offers some awesome ideas for hot sext sessions.

CHEATING? HERE ARE SOME OTHER OPTIONS

This section is for those who have monogamous romantic partners. If you're cheating—or thinking about it—I'd like to offer some alternatives.

I'm not fond of cheating—but as an escort, I sure see a lot of it! Around sixty percent of people (of all genders) cheat on their partners. That means there are probably plenty of folks reading this book who are dating and may have cheated... or who are thinking about it. If you've cheated in the past, you're not alone.

Why do I dislike cheating? Because I hate drama, and I'm a poor liar. Both these things mean that, if I did something dodgy, it would probably end badly.

I understand that not everyone who cheats is an asshole. I see a lot of married clients in the course of my escorting work and sometimes their reasons for straying are surprisingly valid. But it's worth asking yourself if there's a better way. But cheating on your partner is a bit like carrying a stick of dynamite around in your pocket: it might never explode, but just knowing it's there makes you jumpy. Having a romantic partner hidden in your proverbial closet is going to make it difficult for you to present as a decent human being to potential dates.

Remember Dan Savage's campsite rule: leave them better than you found them. This applies to romantic relationships too. Infidelity can leave psychological wounds that take a long time to heal. We're trying to fuck the world better, not fuck it up.

If you care about the person you're dating but can't live without casual flings, ethical non-monogamy is worth consideration.

ETHICAL NON-MONOGAMY:
Having more than one romantic or sexual partner, with the knowledge and consent of everyone involved.

Ethical non-monogamy is the practice of having sex outside your established relationship, with the knowledge and agreement of all your partners. The ways this can happen vary, but here are a few options.

TYPES OF NON-MONOGAMY

- **Open relationship / open marriage**—an agreement between you and your partner that allows one or both of you to play outside your relationship in some way. This may include intercourse, or it might be limited to different types of sex (such as making out, same-sex adventures, or kink activities).

- **Polyamory**—translates roughly to loving many: having relationships with more than one person at a time. There are many ways to practice polyamory, so you probably need to do some research before giving it a go. Check out Further Reading at the end of the book for more sources of information.

- **Monogamish**—describes couples that occasionally relax their monogamy rule. It could mean having threesomes together or occasional flings while travelling. It might mean doing sexy stuff with outside partners but not having PIV intercourse with them. there are so many options… It's a choose-your-own-adventure.

- **DADT (Don't Ask, Don't Tell)**—a form of open relationship where each person is free to play with others, as long as they don't share the details with their partner. I don't recommend this option, because honesty helps most folks feel secure, whereas lying does the opposite. Your mileage may vary.

I practice polyamory—that is, I date more than one person at a time and all my dates and lovers are aware of each other (hell, sometimes they hang out with each other at parties). It's a fun way to do things, because it means

I can cultivate a range of relationships that meet my different needs for sex, kink, affection, and intellectual connection. But it's taken several years to get to this point and I've had to do a lot of work on my communication skills.

Not everyone is cut out for non-monogamy. If you have trust issues or deep insecurities, you may find the emotional work too challenging. Or perhaps it just doesn't suit you—that's okay too. Listen to your fear… don't do anything that makes you feel uncomfortable.

If you're interested in opening your relationship, do it slowly. Read a good book or two on the subject (see Further Reading for details). Talk things over with your partner and check for consent every step of the way. Their response might surprise you—anything from, 'This relationship is over,' to, 'Thank God you asked!' No matter how they respond, trying to rush your partner into an open relationship is a bad idea—it's caused many a breakup. If you feel sure non-monogamy is for you, it's worth taking the time to do it right.

MANAGING AN ONGOING ARRANGEMENT

Remember how I said that feelings are a natural part of hook ups? Sometimes our flings aren't just for one night. Ongoing FWBs (Friends with Benefits) and lover-type arrangements happen too, but they require emotional maturity.

There are many reasons we might seek out an ongoing relationship with someone we're fucking. When you find a good person, it makes sense to hang onto them, even if your interactions aren't headed in a romantic direction.

TYPES OF ONGOING ARRANGEMENTS

- **Friend with benefits**—a mate you occasionally sleep with.
- **Fuck buddy**—a person you're friends with just for the sex.
- **Booty call**—someone you call up at the last minute for sex.
- **Lover**—someone you have an affectionate connection with, but don't date full-time.

Ongoing hook ups are safer and less stressful than meeting new folk all the time. And as you spend more time with someone, you develop a deeper connection, which leads to better sex.

Ongoing arrangements can be confusing. We typically reserve our affection for romantic partners and feel hesitant to show feelings toward casual partners. This is why the word 'relationship' is generally only used for romance—society tells us that anything else isn't worthy of an emotional investment. 'I don't want a relationship' is a common line when someone tries to cut short their date's interest in a potential partnership. If you've used this line before, you're probably not going to like what I say next.

If you have ongoing contact with another person, then you have a relationship with them.

I'm not talking about a capital 'R' relationship—the kind where you say, 'I love you.' But like it or not, if you're boning someone on a regular basis, you're in a relationship of some sort. It might be informal, but it still counts. You owe that person acknowledgement, consideration, and respect, the same as you would for a romantic partner (but with less 'I love you', presumably).

This is why I hate the phrase 'no strings attached.' If you intend to have sex with someone, denying responsibility for their wellbeing is an asshole move. Anyone with whom you get naked deserves considerate treatment. If you try to deny that feelings are involved, you are denying your responsibility. Also, you're wrong—feelings are always involved. It's just a matter of how much.

Feelings are tricky, but pretending they aren't there is pointless. Feelings are not the enemy. If you squash them down, they'll pop up in unexpected ways, such as crying fits during sex or a tantrum when you're out at a nice restaurant (trust me, I've been there).

Navigating a non-romantic relationship requires emotional maturity and communication. It's all about boundaries—being clear on what you and your partner need. This is advanced-level hook-up stuff, so I don't expect you to get it right the first time.

There are so many ways to fuck up relationships! I can't list them all, but here are the most common.

WAYS TO FUCK UP AN ONGOING ARRANGEMENT

- **Acting like your partner is disposable.** This happens when one or both parties decide that 'casual' means 'using', so they behave like jerks. Being unreliable, not caring whether the other person is having a good time, treating them like a second-rate friend… we might not feel as though it matters, but everyone has feelings, whether they're looking for love or not.

- **Trying to manipulate your partner into a romantic relationship.** If someone catches feelings, they may pressure their hook up for a 'real relationship.' This can lead to guilt trips, pushing for more time or seeking declarations of affection… all without directly asking for what they want. That's not okay.

- **Pretending to be tough**. When someone fears commitment, they might treat their partner like shit to prove they aren't interested in romance. Cue ignoring calls, hurtful comments, hiding their partner from their friends… anything to make the point that, 'this isn't a relationship'. Stuff like this is hurtful and unnecessary. If you did your pre-hook-up negotiation properly, it should be clear to everyone that you're not in a romantic relationship. There's no need to be an asshole.

- **'Where is this actually going?'** Sometimes people feel too awkward to even have the pre-sex negotiation. So, the whole time they're seeing each other, they're both wondering, 'Are we dating, or just fucking?' In this situation, people can spend ages worrying over every little social interaction, trying to puzzle out what's going on. It's stressful, and if one person believes the relationship is romantic, they're inevitably going get hurt.

Ongoing casual relationships can be a source of great joy. I've had fuck buddies and lovers for whom I care deeply. In most of these relationships it was clear from the outset exactly what we were doing. But I've fucked up too—usually with lovers, when I wanted a romantic relationship, but was too scared to tell them because I worried that they'd leave me. I've since learned that hiding one's desires from others never works—they sense it, and they feel manipulated. The only way to do it properly is to be honest.

HOW TO HAVE A SUCESSFUL ONGOING ARRANGEMENT

- **Establish an initial agreement.** Get clear on exactly what you both want. Do you just want to meet up for sex? Do you want to hang out and have fun too? Do you enjoy going out to dinner first? Do you prefer to meet once a week, or once a month? Everyone has different needs; there're no right or wrong. But you don't know until you ask.

- **Stick to the rules.** Don't get sloppy with your boundaries— if you've agreed on no contact between dates, don't start calling them in the middle of the night to talk. Don't try to see each other more often than works for both of you. Sometimes our emotions get the better of us; if your partner is the one straying from the rules, gently point it out to them.

- **Check in regularly.** Relationships change over time. You may find your booty call becoming more of a friend, or your fuck buddy turning into a lover. Feelings may grow, lessen, or turn into something entirely different. Often people are scared to admit their needs have changed, so it's important to ask, 'Is this still working for you?' and 'How could we make this thing better?' Depending on the answers, you might need to update your relationship agreement.

- **Don't be afraid to let go.** Like all relationships, hook-up relationships have a shelf life. People and circumstances change, and we don't always have control over where they end up. If the spark is gone or something feels off, you may need to let your partner go so they can move on to new experiences. A relationship ending is not a failure, if it's done respectfully. Letting go of a relationship that's not working will free up more space in your life for the next one to come along.

Polyamory—the practice of having romantic relationships with multiple partners at once—requires many of the same skills as for healthy long-term hook-up arrangements. *The Ethical Slut* by Dossie Easton and Janet Hardy is a comprehensive guide to polyamory that may also help if you want a fuck buddy, lover, or friend with benefits. You can find more books on non-monogamy in the Further Reading section.

TL;DR

- Saying 'no' with honesty, compassion, and confidence is an essential skill that allows you to feel safe and try new things.
- When it comes to flirting, creating respectful distance helps to avoid harassment (that, and picturing your date as a pro wrestler).

- Thinking of cheating? It may be worth considering open relationships instead.
- Long-term hook-up relationships can and do happen. In short: be honest and don't be an asshole.

Mastering advanced social skills isn't easy. It might sound simple on paper, but making these strategies your own requires practice. Be kind to yourself and keep trying—nobody gets it right the first time! I promise you it's worth the work.

If you wish to pursue the advanced sexual escapades in the next chapter, the skills we've just discussed are essential. Whether you're arranging a threesome or being tied up in a dungeon, your social skills will aid you every step of the way.

CHAPTER 11

ADVANCED SEX ADVENTURES

Welcome to the arena! Hopefully, you're now ready to strut your stuff as a sex champion. You're armoured up, your horse is saddled… but is this really a battle? If anything, it's more an exploration; a visit to the circus, contortionism included.

Whatever your preferred metaphor, exiting the world of standard sex can take you to some very interesting places.

The Hellfire Club was one of Sydney's longest-running BDSM events. For more than twenty-five years, it served as a meeting place for kinky people of all persuasions. At the tender age of nineteen, after a dare proposed by a boyfriend, I found myself walking through the club's doors.

Imagine this: a dark corridor. Beyond, a series of dimly lit rooms filled with pounding bass and a sea of exotic human creatures clad in leather, latex, sequins, and lace. I had never seen so many bare asses in my life! Many of these folks sported intimidating equipment—rope, whips, and batons hanging from their belts.

I was too intimidated to speak to anyone, obviously. Finally, a huge guy dressed in a corset and suspenders strode up to me. I prepared to run… but as it turned out he was perfectly friendly.

'I love your dress,' he said. My new friend was a gentle giant who worked in the corporate world during the week but liked to wear ladies' undergarments on the weekend.

That experience taught me a lesson that I've been relearning ever since: average people have an astonishing variety of sexual adventures. You don't have to be some sort of accomplished deviant to love kink clubs. You don't have to be an international playboy to have a threesome. And some suburban housewives own sex toy collections that would put my professional escort associates to shame.

This chapter explains those experiences that some people call scary, but that you can explore with confidence, once you have the know-how. I'll introduce you to the joys of threesomes, share some butt sex techniques, show you how to experiment with kink and, together, we'll find out whether it's worth owning sex toys.

Not all adventures are for everyone. Use your judgement, trust your fear, and let your fantasies guide you. A fun night at the circus? Or just another day in the office? I'll let you decide.

HOW TO DO BUTT SEX...
THE RIGHT WAY

Butt play is common in porn nowadays; many of us have seen it, if not tried it. Some women love anal! For the guys, pegging—being fucked in the ass by someone wearing a strap on—is also popular. Butts can be incredible erogenous zones.

I've met a lot of people who think ass play sucks and don't understand what the fuss is all about. I suspect that some of these folks have been pressured into ass sex, or tried it once but went too fast, and had a bad time. The way you first experience anal affects how enjoyable you find it in the future.

The secret to good anal is feeling relaxed. Butts aren't designed to have things go into them (as opposed to out of them). In order to make it happen, there are two sets of muscles (called sphincters) that need to relax enough for an object to pass through.

The first sphincter is the one you can see from the outside—what you'd technically call your 'butt hole'. The second muscle is further inside. Your butt hole is easy to relax, because those muscles are under your control. It's like your fingers or your mouth: you can move them at will. Getting this area to un-clench is as easy as wishing it so.

The second sphincter—the one further in—is tricky because it's NOT under conscious control. It's like your heart muscle—it does whatever it wants. You can tell yourself to relax until you're blue in the face, but if you feel nervous that inner ring is going to squeeze shut, hard.

When your butt is tense, it's hard to get stuff in there. Being clenched increases the likelihood you'll be damaged, and it means that sex often hurts.

Having a tense rear end is almost guaranteed to make anal play unpleasant instead of enjoyable. Rushing, or forcing things, results in sex that sucks.

Worse, your body remembers past pain and stress. If you try anal and it hurts, then the next time you give it a go, your ass is going to clench up tighter than an over-screwed jar of pickles. This ensures your second experience is bad, which makes your third try worse, and so on.

A lot of harm has been done in the world by folks who think that anal means jamming things into people's butt holes without any preparation. This is why so many people think that anal sex is horrible.

If you're not into anal, you have the right to say 'no'. It's not mandatory: if you don't like it, don't do it. And there could be other stuff going on with your body that means it's not right for you—if you have Irritable Bowel Syndrome (IBS) for example. For some people, anal sex will never be fun, and that's okay.

However, people of all genders do enjoy butt play. For some, it's an occasional adventure. Others use anal stimulation as part of their sex or masturbation routine. If you're interested in giving it a go, there are some steps you can take to help ensure success.

These tips apply to first timers and folks who have tried anal before, although if you've already had a bad experience it's going to take longer, because your body will have some un-learning to do.

STEPS FOR HAVING BETTER BUTT SEX

1. **Use personal lubricant**—Use lube, and lots of it: the rule of thumb is, if you think you're using enough, add more! You can get specialised anal lube from sex shops, and it's well worth the investment.

Otherwise, water-based is great (or silicone, if you're not using silicone toys that will be damaged by silicone lube).

2. **Get to know your body**—Buy a small butt plug and try it. Find the angles that work, and practice relaxing those muscles. Try leaving your toy in for a while so your body can become accustomed. This is about discovering what you like, and about getting used to the sensations associated with anal.

3. **Prepare your butt**—This may or may not be necessary, depending on your diet and how recently you last took a dump. If you think there might be some hangers-on in there, anal douching (flushing your insides with water) is a good idea, if only for your peace of mind. If you don't douche you run the risk of having a shit time, literally. Douching makes it easier to relax - anal sex can make you feel as though you want to poop, and it's helpful knowing you're not actually going to. The easiest way to douche is to use a bulb-shaped device you can buy from a sex shop. Don't go improvising household items to try to get water up your butt! You need something that's designed for the purpose. Search online for instructions. There's also a link to douching advice in the Further Reading section.

4. **Ask your partner to warm you up first**—Get them to use their fingers or small toys before they insert anything bigger such as a cock or a strap on dildo. This stage needs to be slow—take your time and make sure you're feeling relaxed and enjoying yourself, before you move onto the next step. (Or maybe you don't want to move on, maybe this type of play is enough? That's fine too.) Warming up is crucial. If your partner doesn't want to spend time getting you ready, they probably aren't qualified to poke around in such a delicate area.

5. **Go slowly**—Even when you're ready for a larger toy or a cock, take your time. Don't believe what you see in porn—when a porn actor

ass-fucks someone's butt vigorously without lubing it up or going in slowly, they can only do so because of all the preparation that has been done off-camera. Good anal sex requires patience. You want to experiment—move in, then out then a bit further in, and so on. Hold off on the thrusting until your body is used to the feelings. The sensation of fucking (that fast in-out movement) is quite challenging and should be the last thing you attempt, if at all.

6. **Stop whenever you want**—Anal sex is not about 'hanging in there' until someone cums. Like regular sex, there's no point continuing with something if you're not enjoying it. Furthermore, if you start to feel pain, it could be a sign that something is wrong. It's important not to put up with discomfort. Safe words, such as we use for kink play, are useful in this situation. You need to be able to tell your partner when to stop for a moment, or if you wish to stop completely. Anal can be a fun activity even for a short time. There's nothing wrong with having a go and then moving on to other forms of play.

ANAL SAFER SEX

Because the butt is prone to tearing, there's a much higher risk of some STIs spreading during anal sex. It's important you use condoms, both on penises and on toys—this makes clean-up easier too. Don't forget to lube whatever goes in there (lube, lube, and more lube!)

If you feel any pain after anal or see blood (either during sex or when using the toilet afterwards) I'd recommend seeing your doctor. It's easy to tear the lining of your ass. If that happens, you'll need it taken care of. Being embarrassed in front of your GP is preferable to not being able to sit down for a month.

Once an object has been in the ass, it shouldn't go in a pussy or a mouth without being cleaned first. The butt has tons of germs and infections are possible. 'Ass-to-mouth' is another stunt that happens a lot in porn but is a bad idea in real life, for precisely this reason.

Similarly, if you're fingering someone's ass you'll need to wash your hands before you touch their pussy. Latex gloves are useful, because you can just peel them off once you're done with the butt and move on.

If done correctly, butt stuff can be incredible. When you understand the importance of patience and know-how in creating a positive experience, you'll be able to explore this area with enjoyment.

TOYS (OR, WHY THE DOXY IS A STRAIGHT GUY'S BEST FRIEND)

Should you have a sex toy collection? The question is difficult to answer. On the one hand, the more experimentation, the better. I love meeting dates that have a well-stocked bedroom dresser. It suggests more possibilities for play than the standard script.

On the other hand, having an adult arsenal at your disposal can be over-whelming for some folks. A less experienced partner might not be confident playing with toys on a first meeting. You don't want to display bad judgement by freaking someone out the first time you bring them home.

I remember one couple I met during my escort work, who almost managed to freak me out. I was visiting their house for a threesome. On the phone, they said that they were 'a little kinky… nothing too full on.' Imagine my surprise when I arrived to find that an entire wall of their bedroom was hung with kink equipment! Handcuffs, floggers, leather everywhere… they must have spent a fortune on their collection. Clearly, they were more than just 'a little kinky'. I didn't mind them having the stuff, but I felt awkward because they hadn't been honest with me about their level of experience. A less-kinky person might have been upset, and it was irresponsible of them not to warn me first.

Keep your toy collection discreet and exercise your judgement as to when you reveal it. Don't forget to use your consent and communications skills to make sure nobody feels out of their depth.

Here are a few common types of toys, and my thoughts on their usefulness.

- **Dildos**—This term refers to anything that's designed to go in someone's pussy or ass. Insertables are lots of fun, and great for keeping the sex going even if other body parts need to take a break for a while. I recommend purchasing good-quality toys and cleaning them well between uses. Don't appropriate household objects; that's how you end up in the emergency ward. And don't put any toys in the butt that haven't been specifically designed for that purpose. (More on that shortly.)

- **Vibrators**—Sex toys that vibrate are available in a huge variety of shapes, size, and strengths: dildos, eggs, two-person contraptions, and so on. Vibrators are useful for women that have trouble getting to orgasm from penetrative intercourse (that includes most of us). Some guys also like the sensation of vibration.

- **Cock rings** are useful to achieve better erections, and they feel nice, too. They're usually designed to sit around the base of the cock and balls, and they work by restricting blood flow so that blood gets trapped and the erection gets harder. You don't want to leave them on

too long, because restricting blood flow is not good in the long term.
But a lot of penis owners say cock rings enhance their sensation.

- **Pumps and suction devices** can be fun to play with. There are large
  ones for cocks, and small ones for clits. I should note, I've never
  heard of anyone pulling out a penis pump in the middle of a sexual
  encounter (if you have, then more power to you). But clit suction can
  be amazing—it's a type of stimulation that's unlike anything other
  types of toys can provide. Clit suction devices are small, portable,
  and usually rechargeable. They make a great addition to regular sex.

- **'Couples' Toys'**—Lots of toys are designed to fit into, over, or around
  heterosexual couples during sex. Some of them look like space-
  age objects (and cost almost as much as one of Elon Musk's space
  missions). Getting couples' toys to work can be tricky, and I recommend you read the manual before you give them a go. Personally, I
  find couples' toys too fiddly to use during a one-night stand. I prefer
  to save them for ongoing relationships, once trust has been established.

- **Strap ons**—These are harnesses that fit around the crotch region;
  they usually look like an abseiling harness, but there are also ones
  that look like underwear. They are designed to hold dildos in place
  for the purpose of fucking someone else. Strap ons allow people who
  don't have cocks to enjoy the experience of penetrating their partner.
  They are most commonly used by pussy-owners fucking other peeps
  with pussies, or couples who enjoy pegging (see 'kinks' for more
  info).

EVERY WOMAN'S BEST FRIEND: THE POCKET VIBE

These days, you can purchase vibrators that are waterproof, rechargeable,
and no bigger than a tube of lipstick. Even though they're small, they still

offer a strong vibration. These are great for throwing in your handbag on the way to a date, in case you need some assistance to get to orgasm. For folk that require maximum power, I'd recommend the next option…

EVERY MAN'S BEST FRIEND: THE MASSAGE WAND
If I could put a massage wand in the bedroom of every straight guy in the country, I would do it. Forget the cost, forget every other sex toy on the market: if you're serious about making clits happy, this toy is a great investment.

Sometimes it's known as a 'Hitachi' or 'Hitachi Magic Wand' because that's the name of the earliest available appliance. The Hitachi was originally sold as a therapeutic device for cramped muscles (like your back, I mean.) Nowadays, there are other varieties designed specifically for sexual pleasure.

A massage wand has a large vibrating head and long handle. It usually has an electrical cord that plugs into a wall socket, although some smaller versions are cordless. This device is remarkable in its ability to help many women orgasm. It takes barely any effort—all you must do is ensure it's placed near the right area.

This toy isn't super portable. It's hard to take on a casual date (when I go on escort jobs, it travels in a suitcase). But it's an amazing thing to have in your bedroom. I'm noticing a growing trend for young, hetero guys to own one, simply to ensure they can satisfy their hook ups. When I visit couples, I take my wand with me because it helps ensure I get my female clients off. If you own a Hitachi, you can forget about the 'women are hard to please' stereotype: with this tool and some good communication, you're 95% there.

It should be noted that not all women love the device—sometimes it's too strong, if they're particularly sensitive. Ask first and start on the lowest setting.

The Mercedes of the massage wand world is called a Doxy Wand. Mine is steel-plated and when I switch it on, it vibrates like an airplane engine. It's the best investment I've ever made.

CLEANING YOUR TOYS

Toys should be washed after every use. Most toys can be safely cleaned in warm, soapy water, depending on the manufacturer's instructions. I also recommend spraying them with a toy-safe disinfectant such as Viraclean or VibeClean—these are available from sex shops. Note that putting condoms on any insertable toys before use will reduce wear and make the clean-up job easier.

WHERE TO GET YOUR TOYS

If you're lucky enough to live in a big city, you'll be spoiled for choice when you visit an adult store in person. Sex shops have become remarkably professional in recent years—there are great stores out there, with nice lighting and female-friendly staff. But even if you visit your dingy subterranean local, you'll usually find the people who work there to be knowledgeable. If you're serious about buying, they're usually happy to help.

If you're shy or live in a remote location, online stores have a huge range— the only problem being, you can't check out the merchandise first. If you're not sure about the quality of an item, do a Google search for reviews. Reviews are a great way to learn more before you blow all your savings on the latest device.

Make sure your mail is tracked—I had a delivery stolen from the front of my apartment building once! I have no idea what the thief did with that chin-strap dildo… I reckon they were really confused when they opened the box.

HOW TO HAVE A SPECTACULAR THREESOME

Threesomes are a bit like dragons… they're mythical creatures we've heard about, but that most people have never laid eyes on. I've got some good news for you: threesomes happen all the time.

I know, because they happen to me.

My first threesome occurred when I was twenty-two, during a walk through a cemetery in Sydney with a couple of my friends. We were weird little Goth kids. We liked hanging out in graveyards because we thought it was super cool. When my two guy friends started making out, I thought, 'what the hell'…and then we all banged behind a tombstone. An embarrassing cliché, yes… but it was the nineties, after all.

My first experience was a male/male/female (MMF) threesome. Threesomes also come in plenty of other varieties, such as the classic MFF (the one you often see in porn.) Three-ways are becoming more mainstream these days; lots of folks are giving it a go. I often organise these experiences as part of my escorting work. There's even a dating app for finding partners (taking 'there's an app for that' to a whole new level!)

'HOW DO I GET A THREESOME HAPPENING?'

I have a friend who says, 'the best way to hit on a woman is to wait for the woman to hit on you.' This principle applies to threesomes. If you're a heterosexual guy, it's almost impossible to get an MFF happening unless the ladies are just as keen as you. Don't believe what pickup artists tell you—getting some female friends together and dropping hints is basically social suicide.

People dislike that approach for a reason. When we hunt down someone to fulfil our own personal fantasies, we often forget about the needs of others. Sex should be about what everyone wants—being fixated on a threesome suggests to potential partners that you're not interested in them as people. It's a selfish, single-minded attitude, and it's massive a turnoff. If a threesome happens, it's because everyone wants it to happen.

Even couples that are looking for a third can run into trouble. As a single, bisexual woman, there's nothing more annoying than coming out to a couple and immediately receiving an invitation fuck them, as though that's all I'm useful for. Bisexual women who want to fuck hetero couples are known by a specific term: unicorns. As in, extremely rare. It's difficult to find one, and if you go around asking all the time, you're going to piss everyone off.

The Internet is useful for finding enthusiastic partners. Online classifieds and dating apps can work to find thirds, provided you're honest about what you want. There's even an app called *Feeld*. Doing it this way means you can advertise yourself without harassing folks who'd rather be left out of your sexual fantasies.

As always, respect is key. Having a threesome isn't just about ticking an item off your bucket list—the people you're hoping to fuck want something out of it too. If you start treating them as though they're your own personal porn actor, you're going to be a bad lover and the threesome will suck. Treat prospective partners the same as you would any other date—meet them in public, establish a good connection, do your pre-hook-up negotiation. Talk about your needs and give them time to talk about theirs.

If you're struggling to find a partner, a sex worker is a great option, albeit a little more expensive. Sex workers are great for first timers—it's helpful when someone in the room knows what they're doing! If you find a professional that you connect with and treat them with respect, the encounter can be every bit as enjoyable as if you'd picked someone up online... or better, thanks to our professional confidence and expertise.

Once you find yourself on a potential threesome date, success depends on how well everyone gets along. This applies particularly to anyone who is nervous or undecided—if one or more of your partners doesn't feel enthusiastic, things probably won't go well. In this way, it's more about letting a threesome happen than making it happen. Allow connection to develop, ask openly for what you want, and wait to see how events unfold.

'HOLY SHIT, A THREESOME IS HAPPENING! WHAT DO I DO?'

Is everyone feeling good about it? If so, the easiest way to ensure a good time is to let go of your expectations. One of the reasons threesomes are so fun is that it's a different social dynamic. It's less a private moment, more of a group project.

Threesome sex is always off script. You can't follow a sex script that's written for two people, when three are involved. Forget all your ideas about positions and orgasms and who should cum when, where, and how... do what feels right in the moment. Now is the time to use all those communication skills we talked about in Part I (I hope you've been practising!) Get feedback by asking, 'How does that feel?' And surrender to the fact that you probably won't always know what you're doing.

Don't worry about how things 'should' be going. It's not about recreating the last porn scene you watched. It's just about being mindful and experimenting until you discover what works.

The complexity of managing everyone at once can be nerve-wracking—more consent requirements, more dangers, more drama if things go wrong. If you're socially anxious, a threesome could be overwhelming (unless you plan on hiring two sex workers, in which case you'll most likely be in safe hands).

Like all sex, threesomes can be silly or awkward… and when they're awkward they are particularly so, because there are more people to notice those long silences. The key to surviving is to understand that awkwardness and fumbling are inevitable. You can call attention it if you want, in radical honesty fashion: 'Ha ha! Awkward threesome sex!' Then get on with it. Don't let awkwardness ruin your date.

Here are my favourite strategies for ensuring a good three-way.

GEORGIE'S HOT THREESOME SEX TIPS

- **Keep the pack together.** Humans are pack animals, and this becomes more apparent in a threesome situation. There's always a 'top dog'—someone who is the most confident. And there's always an 'underdog'—the person who is nervous, vulnerable or most likely to feel threatened. In a good threesome, the top dog will look after the underdog and make sure everything moves at a pace that is com-fortable for them. When I do MFF threesomes at work, I'm usually the top dog: I'm experienced, confident and being paid to manage the experience. The 'underdog' is usually the wife or girlfriend, because she may feel nervous about being with another woman or worry that I'm going to steal her partner's attention. My efforts are devoted to ensuring she feels respected and comfortable. Sometimes the underdog isn't the other woman—sometimes it's a guy who feels insecure. If the threesome has a different gender mix, it may be the physically smaller person or the younger person who need looking after. Of course, I'm not suggesting the third person (the one in the middle) should be neglected. But by giving a little more attention to the underdog, you drastically decrease the risk of shit going wrong.

- **The two-hand trick**—in the best threesomes, nobody gets left on the sidelines. I always ensure I maintain contact with both partners. This sometimes means using my hands (e.g., giving someone a hand job while I'm going down on someone else), or sometimes it's just about making eye contact or resting a friendly hand on someone's thigh. It's my way of saying, 'I know you're still here, even if we're not interacting closely right now.'

- **Respect your straight mate**—if you're in a threesome with two straight people (such as an MMF where the guys are straight, or an MFF where the women are), then the contact doesn't need to be physical. Eye contact, nods, high fives, planning your next moves together, having a laugh… All these send the message that the other person is included. Guys, making eye contact with your best mate while you're both boning a chick does not automatically make you gay. There's no need to get weird about it.

THREESOME SAFER SEX

Safer sex is tricky when there's more than two. It's hard to keep an eye on where all those hands, toys, and genitals are going. The basic rules are:

- **Use condoms on all your toys** and change the condom every time you start using it on a different partner.
- **Same for dicks**—condoms get changed every time the cock-owner switches between people.
- **Be aware of where your hands go.** If you touch someone's sticky bits with one hand, then touch someone else's (including your own), you can spread STIs. You can avoid this by using the left hand for one person and the right for another, or by using baby wipes or washing your hands between partners.
- **Consider using insertive condoms.** Insertive condoms (also knowns as femidoms) are worn inside the vagina or butt, thereby

allowing one cock-owner to fuck multiple partners without changing condoms. Of course, if more than one cock is involved then this approach won't work. But for scenarios such as MFF threesomes, it's pretty neat. I'd like to thank to escort Alice Grey for this pro tip!

'DOES IT EVER GO WRONG?'

I've had awkward threesomes. I've been in situations where one of the women started crying halfway through and we had to stop and talk. Sometimes I get tired and have to tap out—three-ways can be exhausting!

Threesomes aren't supposed to look like porn scenes. They are the same as any other type of sex—silly, unpredictable, hot, awkward, and exciting. Being open to the possibilities is crucial. If you expect an encounter to match up to that porn movie in your head, you're going to be disappointed. But if you stay chill and experiment, threesomes can be incredible.

Likewise, they come with the same pitfalls as regular sex… but the potential for drama is greater. The 'Freak Outs and Breakdowns' section in Chapter 9 is essential reading, if you're worried about managing a threesome gone wrong. And if you doubt your ability to handle a threesome meltdown, you should probably reconsider trying this stuff in the first place.

'WHAT ABOUT MORE THAN THREE?'

Beyond threesomes, we have group sex. Group sex can involve any number of participants and can take many forms, such as wife swapping at your local swingers' club, sex party orgies, or gang bangs. Group sex is advanced territory—getting consent from many people at once is complicated. It involves a lot of negotiating beforehand, and the use of specialised safe words.

If you go in this direction, you may be moving beyond the scope of this book. These situations are best learned in person; consider doing a workshop or find some experienced, trustworthy people and ask them to show you the way forward.

KINK & ROUGH SEX

Kink is entering the mainstream more than ever before—consider *Fifty Shades of Grey* and all those steamy romance novels on Amazon. People are becoming more open-minded… that's a good thing. But when it comes to kink, safety is an issue. You need to know what you're doing.

> **KINK:** Any sexy stuff that's 'out of the ordinary' (whatever that means...)

Kink is any sexual behaviour that falls outside the norm (whatever that's supposed to mean). Kink is also referred to as BDSM (Bondage, Domination, Submission, Sadism and Masochism), D/S (Domination/Submission) and B&D (Bondage and Domination). We (by which I mean myself and other kinky bastards) use the term 'kink' to describe a broad range of sexy stuff that isn't regular romantic sex. It can include:

- **Sensation/Pain play**: includes non-painful fun such as teasing, touching… or for the more adventurous, it can mean spanking, hitting, whipping, flogging, slapping, using either hands or special-ised implements.
- **Bondage**—tying people up / restraining them in some way or being tied/restrained.

- **Domination and submission**—directing your partner or letting them direct you.
- **Fetishes**—wearing clothing such as leather or latex or being hot for specific objects, scenarios, or parts of the body.
- **Water sports**—peeing on someone, or vice versa.
- **Pegging**—fucking someone in the ass using a strap on.
- **Role play**—enacting a sexy scenario by taking on character roles (cop/robber, nurse/patient, etc.)

This is an incomplete list. Kink includes so many possibilities—if your interest doesn't appear above, it's not because you're unusual!

When practising kink, we say that the person doing the stuff is the 'top' and the person receiving is the 'bottom.' We might also use the word 'dominant' to describe the person who's in control, and 'submissive' to describe the person giving up control. Sometimes it isn't clear who's in charge, but when it is, we call it 'power exchange' because one person is temporarily giving up a bit of their power to the other person. We also sometimes use the terms 'master' or 'mistress' to describe the person who has agreed to call the shots.

Some people might not necessarily say they are into kink but still get up to rough stuff that is technically BDSM, such as biting, wrestling, or slapping. If this is you, be aware that you need to practice all the same safety skills as if you were going around calling yourself 'Master Spank-a-Lot.'

I know a lady friend who was accustomed to having wild sex with her fuck buddy. He'd made a few comments about liking it rough, so one day she decided to slap him in the face mid-coitus.

Well, that freaked him right out. He got upset, put his clothes on and left. Later, he told her that it had hurt, and that slapping wasn't something he enjoyed. My friend felt bad but couldn't understand what she had done wrong—she assumed that by saying he was into rough sex, he was indicating he'd be okay with a slap in the face.

She assumed wrong. The phrase 'rough sex' means different things to different people. You can't walk up to someone in the street and slap them—that's assault. So why is the bedroom any different?

Getting clear consent is the first step before engaging in anything kink-related. You do this the same way you get consent for anything else: by asking and then giving your partner time to say 'yes' or 'no'.

When you do kink, the stakes are much higher than for regular sexual encounters. In addition to violating someone's physical boundaries, you could also be doing them extreme physical and emotional harm. A fuck-up could mean having the cops at your door or ending up in the emergency ward. It's important that you communicate clearly.

Luckily, consent talk goes well with kinky sex. It's easy (and hot) to say, 'I'm going to hold you down and have my way with you, what do you say to that?' You don't even have to sound nice about it, if you've both agreed to play the role of dominant/submissive. You just need to give your partner a chance to say 'yes' or 'no'.

KINK IS NOT ABUSE

Due to some badly written books and crappy movies, there's sometimes this idea among regular folk that kink is about one person getting to do whatever they want to their unsuspecting partner. Taking what you want might seem sexy as a fantasy, but that's not what kink is about.

If you're confused, I understand. Kink is meant to look scary—often, one person is playing the role of the helpless victim and the other is enjoying doing wicked things to them. But these are just characters—the adult equivalent of cops and robbers. In reality, the person receiving (the 'bottom' or 'submissive') is the one who gets the final say over what happens to them.

In kink play, it's the top/dominant's job to give the sub/bottom what they want. I don't mean that you should go make them a cup of tea. What I mean is, the dominant should only be doing things that both the dominant and submissive enjoy. If the submissive enjoys spanking, give them a spanking. If they enjoy being humiliated, call them names. Keep checking in to make sure they are still having fun. Likewise, the dominant must be enjoying themselves.

In kink, everyone needs to be having fun; it's just that some people's idea of 'fun' is being whipped, slapped, or ordered around. Don't be fooled into thinking that anyone is being abused.

On the other hand: if someone is doing things to you that you've said 'no' to, or making you do things to them that you don't want to do, that's sexual assault. It's not kink, and it's not okay. The same rules apply, whether you're having missionary-position sex or running around the house in assless chaps.

SAFE WORDS FOR ADVANCED CONSENT

Kinksters who know their stuff always have a safe word: a code word either person can say to stop play, for any reason. I use the traffic light system of green, orange and red, as described in Chapter Seven.

TRAFFIC LIGHT SAFE WORDS

- **'Green'** means, 'Yes, this is great! Keep going!'
- **'Orange'** means, 'I don't like this specific activity,' or, 'I've reached my limit, don't go any harder.'
- **'Red'** means, 'Everything must stop now!'

I used to be awkward at pre-sex negotiations. Even now I sometimes start making out with someone and have to stop and get their safe words before we start getting into the rough stuff. Usually I'll say, 'do you know the traffic light system?' and if they don't, I'll give them a quick run-down.

Once someone is clued in, I'll say, 'are we green?' This is the kink equivalent of the 'how does this feel?' that you learned in the chapter on consent. Once you have a 'green' you know it's safe to proceed, but slowly and with caution, while checking in regularly.

'STARTER' KINK

Here are some kinky activities that don't pose too much of a physical risk, if you start gently.

- **Spanking**—slapping someone's ass with your hand is fun and safe, as long as you avoid the tailbone (the area at the top of the butt crease where the spine ends). Start lighter than light and gradually increase the intensity—this warms up the skin and prepares your partner. Spanking can be a fun disciplinary manoeuvre, or it can be used to lull someone into a trance, as they relax and enjoy the sensation. Experiment with different places on the ass and get feedback from your partner ('How does this feel?')

- **Physical restraint**—holding someone's wrists above their head or wrapping your arms around them and squeezing their body… fun, and reasonably safe because you can release them at any time. As with all things, start gently. It's still possible to bruise someone or even break bones, if you squeeze too hard.

- **Verbal commands**—ah, the essence of dominance/submission! I love it when my partners tell me what to do, especially if it's delivered with a bit of sexy confidence. Commands could be as simple as asking them to take their clothes off, or as complicated as instructing them how to give you head. It takes practice to sound like you know what you're doing; don't feel bad if your first few attempts aren't as sexy as you hoped. For bonus points, take turns giving each other instructions. It's nice to try both roles and see what you enjoy the most.

KINK ACTIVITIES TO AVOID

Some kink and rough sex activities are common, but inadvisable. Even though they seem straightforward, they're dangerous.

Don't believe me? Ask my friend Rebecca. She's a super-smart and adventurous twenty-five-year-old who loves trying new things… but she deeply regrets one of her first encounters with kink. After meeting a boyfriend who was into BDSM, Rebecca suggested they try some new stuff together. It started off well: her partner was safe and respectful. They tried anal play, toys, and other fun stuff. But over time, things started to get a bit risky.

She told me, 'The problem was that we enjoyed drinking together, and that wasn't safe at all. Alcohol can lower inhibitions, so even though something might seem like a good idea at the time, it's definitely not.'

One evening they decided to try breath play, in the form of choking. It's an activity commonly seen in mainstream porn—if you watch a lot of porn, it might seem normal to just grab your partner by the throat. But in real life, choking is dangerous—so dangerous that many experienced kinksters won't do it. Although Rebecca and her partner were trying to be careful, they were both drunk, and the situation escalated. Her partner choked her until she lost consciousness. When she woke up, she had suffered severe damage to her throat; she began vomiting blood. A doctor would later tell her that she may have suffered minor brain damage.

After that night, she never spoke to her ex-partner again. 'It made it really hard to trust another person, because I could have died,' she said.

When it comes to kink, sometimes it's a bad idea to rush in without doing your research first. Not knowing your shit might result in serious harm to someone you care about.

Here are a few things that, as a beginner, I recommend you avoid.

- **Face slapping**—it's much more dangerous that one might think. If you hit the person while their neck isn't braced, they can suffer whiplash. Or, if your hand lands on their ear, you might break their eardrum and cause permanent deafness. Face slapping is a common form of domestic violence, so if your partner has been abused as a child or by a partner in the past then you might seriously traumatise them. (And who brings up that sort of story on the first date? You don't know who has suffered domestic violence and who hasn't.) Some kink experts do enjoy face slapping, and it can be great if it's done well—but you need the knowledge on how to do it first. It's not a beginner move.

- **Choking is considered one of the most dangerous of all kink activities.** If you put your hand around someone's neck, you squash the carotid arteries on the side of the neck and cut off blood to the brain. The longer the brain is starved of blood (and therefore oxygen), the more likely your partner is to suffer brain damage or stroke. It can happen quickly, long before they pass out. In addition, the front of the throat has cartilage that, if crushed, will block air from getting to the lungs. This is irreversible—if you squeeze someone's throat too hard and their windpipe collapses, they will choke to death in front of you and you won't be able to do a damn thing about it. Choking is never safe; even experienced kinksters often avoid it. It's becoming more and more common among folks who like rough sex. But it can kill. Please don't attempt it without some serious research.

- **Bondage with household objects**—Okay, first I need to say, *never let someone you've just met tie you up!* Bondage is dangerous because it leaves you at the mercy of whomever you're playing with. If you don't know them well, never let them put you in any situation you can't get out of.

  If you've known someone for a while, you may trust them enough to experiment with bondage. But I recommend buying the right equipment, rather than using common household objects. Sometimes folks want to start simply, so they use a scarf or rope or whatever they have lying around. But wrists and ankles are delicate; that scarf that seems light and friendly can become excruciatingly painful when it's stretched tight. The same applies to those novelty handcuffs you can buy at sex shops: the hard metal can cut into flesh and cause serious injury. If you want to tie people up, the safest way is to invest in some wide leather wrist cuffs from a sex or kink store. They look scary, but in fact they are a much safer option.

  Some experienced kinksters love using rope, but you need to learn how to use it before you start tying people—consult Further Reading to learn more.

NEED MORE INFORMATION?

Think you might be interested in kink? There are plenty of ways to learn. Check out the Further Reading section at the back of this book for suggestions. You may also be able to find support groups and workshops, if you're in a big city. Whatever happens, don't try anything you're unsure about—do your research first.

HOW TO HOOK UP WITH SEX WORKERS

Sex workers are one of Australia's most under-utilised resources. I should know... I've been working as an escort for almost eight years. In that time, I have helped people lose their virginities, taught guys how to give good head, introduced people to kink, gifted couples with their first threesomes, and counselled clients through hard times in their lives. Sex work is much more than just fucking people for money. Sometimes sex work isn't about fucking at all...

A sex worker is someone who provides sexual services in exchange for payment. The term includes (but isn't limited to) street sex workers, parlour workers, erotic dancers, massage workers (of the 'rub-n-tug' variety), peep-show performers, doms/dominatrices, escorts, cam artists, and sexological bodyworkers. Some of these jobs involve penetrative sex, some involve a hand job, and some (such as strippers) might not include touching.

> **SEX WORK:** Providing sexy experiences for payment.

REASONS TO SEE A SEX WORKER

- **If you're socially awkward** and you need to practice your skills with someone who will be kind to you.
- **If you haven't gotten laid in a while**, and you're starting to feel desperate (looking desperate has ruined many a promising date).
- If you have a particular kink or fetish, but you can't find anyone else who is into it.

- **If you want to try something new** (such as a kink or sex act, or even just getting the hang of different positions).
- **If you desire a threesome** but can't find suitable partners.
- If you're interested in sex with someone who has a **particular type of body or appearance** that might be difficult to find in your regular life.

Sex work is legal in most states of Australia. If you're not sure about the legalities in your location, check out some the sex work websites listed in the Further Reading section.

Sex professionals come in a variety of ages, genders and body types. The right worker can guide you through a sexual encounter, give you how-to advice, and plan an experience that addresses your specific interests. It's okay to ask for what you want—our work is meant to fulfil your needs, which is why you pay—as opposed to a regular date, where everyone's desires are equally important.

That's not to say we don't have needs at all, however. When you see a sex worker, you're not purchasing sex. You're purchasing our time and sex-pertise, and the chance to have a specific type of encounter. How well that encounter proceeds depends on your behaviour. Connection, consent, and honesty are still essential. You must treat your worker like a human being.

STEPS TO SEEING A SEX WORKER

1. **Find the right person for you.** Depending on your state, there are many ways to find people. I recommend an internet search, as this turns up many options. Some states allow brothels (a venue with private rooms and workers available). Other sex workers are available independently or through escort agencies, and these folks may come to you or require you visit them at their apartment or hotel. Sex workers all have different skills and personalities. Spend some

time speaking with your chosen person (if only via email, or a quick chat on the phone) to make sure they suit you. If something isn't feeling right or you're not making a connection, don't be afraid to try someone else.

2. **Do your research.** Make sure your potential professional offers what you're looking for. Read their advertisement thoroughly (or ask the staff of the establishment when you arrive) so that you don't ask too many silly questions. This includes how much it will cost and what sort of services are on offer. As with a regular date, there's no point wasting your time on someone who doesn't fit your needs. Prices range from affordable to top-dollar, so don't assume you can't afford to see a sex worker; check it out first!

3. **Be a great communicator.** When you speak with the worker—whether in person or via phone or email—be honest and specific about experience you want (whether it's 'I just want to get laid' or 'I need someone to show me how to do anal sex'). The more specific you are, the easier it will be for your person to tell whether they are right for you. Not everyone offers all services, and they will tell you right away if they can't provide what you're looking for. Keep asking until you find the right person. Also, when planning a session ahead of time, have specific dates in mind. We get time wasters all the time in this business; if you aren't specific about when and where you'd like to meet, we may assume you're not serious. Sex workers often have booking guidelines on their ads or websites. Things will be easier for everyone if you follow their instructions and safety protocols.

4. **Treat it like a regular date.** Take a shower, put on your best shirt, and bring your hook-up game. Just because you're paying doesn't mean you don't need to make an effort. A sex worker, like any person, has the right to refuse sex (or indeed anything else) if they

think you're not up to standard, or if you're being an asshole. Sex workers are generally tolerant and understanding—being bigger than average in the waist department, older, married, or socially anxious usually won't be a problem. But you still need to be doing your best. The more effort you put in, the better service you'll receive.

5. **Use your consent skills.** Sex with sex workers is the same as with any other person. We have the right to say 'no' to anything we don't like, even if it's something we have previously agreed to. We're allowed to stop at any time. And you still want your partner to have a good time, even if you're paying them to take good care of you. Get consent and check in often. Some folks feel that paying a sex worker means they're entitled to do whatever they want to them; that's not how it works. Practising consent with sex workers is just as import-ant as it is with friends and partners.

6. **Show your appreciation.** Like any professional, sex workers love good feedback. It doesn't have to come in the form of a cash tip or gift (although that's lovely). Just a genuine 'thank you' will make us feel as though we've done a good job.

Sex workers are like everyone else: we all deserve respectful and honest treatment. In my work, I've found that the best encounters happen when my clients treat a booking the same as any other date. Establish a good connection first, make an effort, and you'll find that your experience can be just as rewarding.

TL;DR
- Anal sex can be an incredible experience for all genders. But go slow, or you'll fuck yourself (or someone else) up.
- A toy collection can be a great asset, if it's deployed appropriately.

- Threesomes: keep the pack together! And pay attention to safer sex, because it looks different when there are more than two players.
- Kink includes a diverse range of fetishes and activities. Do your research before you play, be honest about your level of experience, and use your consent skills.
- Sex workers are a fantastic resource. As above, do your research first… and treat us with consideration, the same as you would any other hook-up partner.

Not all adventures suit everyone… but I hope this chapter has sparked your interest for further explorations. Life is too short to stay in your comfort zone! If you have the confidence and the skills to match, why not try something new?

If you encountered an escapade in this chapter that you're particularly interested in trying, I'd recommend more research. Check out the Further Reading section at the end of this book—I've included websites and books for each of the topics we've discussed.

IN CONCLUSION

Welcome to the end... well, kinda.

So far, you've built psychological armour. You've learned how to drive your sex life further. And then, because you're awesome, you've tackled the stuff that will turn you into a sexual champion, someone who can make the world a better place.

You may have put some of this information into practice as you've been reading, or you might just now be feeling ready to get out there and give it a go. Here's my final piece of advice: don't expect to get it right every time. When it comes to hook ups, I still fuck up royally sometimes. And despite my confidence, I still feel awkward. I'm a human being—that's just how it is.

Being great at sex means accepting your imperfections. Trying to win every time is a fool's game; if you think you're going to hook up with every person you swipe right on, you're setting yourself up for failure. And if you set the expectation of mind-blowing sex with every single sexual partner every single time, you might collapse under the pressure.

Don't panic or beat yourself up if you blurt out something inappropriate on a first date or get unmatched ten times in a row. It happens to the best of us. You're not supposed to be perfect.

Here's the good news: by making the effort, you're way ahead of the game.

Hardly anyone in the dating scene practices this stuff, so it's easy to put yourself ahead of the competition. Hell, just by reading this book you've learned more about sex than most of the singles I've ever encountered. If you practice these skills, the people you hook up with will notice... and it's going to make a difference to your sex life.

You know that moment where you pause, take a deep breath, wipe your sweaty palms, and usher someone new into your bedroom? I still feel nervous when I'm about to get laid, but I no longer hesitate. As my gym coach says, it doesn't get easy... you just get better. Our efforts DO pay off—we find better people, make better connections, and have better encounters. One date at a time, we're learning to be sexual superstars.

That's all from me, folks. Now get out there! Spread the word as well as the love... and enjoy your hook ups!

FURTHER READING

Ready to learn more? Here are some starting points for further research.

HEAD SKILLS & LIFE LESSONS

- *This Is How: Proven Aid in Overcoming Shyness, Molestation, Fatness, Spinsterhood, Grief, Disease, Lushery, Decrepitude & More. For Young and Old Alike*, Augusten Burroughs

- *Daring Greatly: How the Courage to Be Vulnerable Transforms the Way We Live, Love, Parent, and Lead*, Brené Brown

- *The Gift of Fear*, Gavin De Becker

- *The Subtle Art of Not Giving a Fuck*, Mark Manson

CONSENT & COMMUNICATION

- 'Consent: It's Simple as Tea' |
  https://www.youtube.com/watch?v=fGoWLWS4-kU

- *Crucial conversations: Tools for Talking When Stakes are High*, Al Switzler, Joseph Grenny and Ron McMillan

- 'The Rock Test', Anne Victoria Clark | https://medium.com/@anne-victoriaclark/the-rock-test-a-hack-for-men-who-dont-want-to-be-accused-of-sexual-harassment-73c45e0b49af\

- 'The Experimental Generation of Human Closeness' on *Psychology Today* | https://www.psychologytoday.com/au/blog/open-gen-tly/201310/36-questions-bring-you-closer-together

SEX SKILLS

- *Sexting: The Grownup's Little Book of Sex Tips for Getting Dirty Digitally*, Tina Horn

- 'Smart Sex Resource' by the British Columbia Center for Disease Control | https://smartsexresource.com/

- 'How to Clean Your Ass Before Anal Sex' | https://howtoclean-yourass.wordpress.com/

- Curious Creatures | http://www.curiouscreatures.biz

KINK AND BDSM

- *The New Topping Book*, Dossie Easton & Janet W. Hardy

- *The New Bottoming Book,* Dossie Easton & Janet W. Hardy

- *SM 101: A Realistic Introduction*, Jay Wiseman

- Kink Academy | www.kinkacademy.com

RELATIONSHIPS AND OPEN RELATIONSHIPS

- The Savage Lovecast | https://www.savagelovecast.com/

- *The Ethical Slut: A Practical Guide to Polyamory, Open Relationships & Other Adventures*, Janet W. Hardy & Dossie Easton

- *Opening Up: A Guide to Creating and Sustaining Open Relationships*, Tristan Taormino

DIVERSITY

- 'The Gender Unicorn' at Trans Student Education Resources | http://www.transstudent.org/gender/

- *Queer Sex: A Trans and Non-Binary Guide to Intimacy, Pleasure and Relationships*, Juno Roche

- 'Your First Time: What to Expect When Seeing an Escort' | https://scarletblue.com.au/guest-blog/first-time-expect-seeing-escort

ABOUT THE AUTHOR

Georgie Wolf is an Aussie escort, writer and educator.

Hailing from Sydney, she's worked as an adult store salesperson, a designer of porn catalogues, and a pin up photographer. Nowadays, she's an independent escort based in Melbourne.

She writes, speaks, and coaches... and loves sharing first date stories with friends, over a glass of red.

Learn more at:

WWW.ARTOFTHEHOOKUP.COM

DID YOU ENJOY THE BOOK?
PLEASE LEAVE A REVIEW!

As an independent author, my work lives or dies by your support. With every review or word-of-mouth recommendation, we're getting this information to the people who need it.

Please leave a review by visiting www.amazon.com.au.

Got feedback? I'd love to hear from you. You can reach me via email: **info@artofthehookup.com.**